Engineering Properties of Rocks

Engineering Properties of Rocks

I. W. Farmer
B.Sc., Ph.D., M.I.C.E., A.M.I.M.M., F.G.S.

LONDON
E. & F. N. SPON LTD
1968

First published 1968 by
E. & F. N. Spon Limited
11 New Fetter Lane, London E.C.4
© *Ian William Farmer 1968*
Printed in Great Britain by
Butler & Tanner Ltd, Frome and London

Distributed in the U.S.A.
by Barnes & Noble Inc.

Contents

Preface   *page* ix

Nomenclature   x

Introduction   1

1. Chemical and Physical Rock Properties   4
    1.1 *Composition of rocks*   4
    1.2 *Geological classification of rocks*   8
    1.3 *Rock structure*   11
    1.4 *Pore space in rock*   15

2. Stress and Strain   17
    2.1 *Stress at a point*   17
    2.2 *Combined stress analysis*   20
    2.3 *Strain at a point*   23
    2.4 *Strain ellipse*   25
    2.5 *Stress/strain relationship*   28

3. Elastic Properties of Rocks   30
    3.1 *Stress/strain relationship in an elastic medium*   30
    3.2 *Elasticity of rocks*   33
    3.3 *Elastic constants for rocks*   36
    3.4 *Elastic theory applied to design in rock*   40

4. Rheological Properties of Rocks   41
    4.1 *Rheological models*   41
    4.2 *Flow in rocks*   45
    4.3 *Flow properties of rocks*   50
    4.4 *Creep as a design factor in rock*   53

5. Strength and Failure in Rocks   55
    5.1 *Uniaxial strength*   55
    5.2 *Strength of rocks in confinement*   58
    5.3 *Mohr criterion of failure*   63
    5.4 *Griffith criterion of brittle failure*   65

6. Dynamic Properties of Rocks   70

   6.1 Wave propagation in a rock mass   70
   6.2 Oscillatory wave motion in rock   76
   6.3 Stress and strain in waves   78
   6.4 Reflection of stress waves   80
   6.5 Dynamic strength of rocks   81
   6.6 Deformation processes under dynamic loading   83

7. Rock Testing   86

   7.1 Laboratory testing – specimen preparation   86
   7.2 Laboratory tests – stress/strain characteristics   87
   7.3 Laboratory tests – strength   90
   7.4 Triaxial testing   92
   7.5 Field testing   95
   7.6 Accuracy of test data   100

8. Effect of Water on Rock Properties   102

   8.1 Flow of water through rocks   102
   8.2 Effect of water on rock strength   104
   8.3 Effect of water on rock deformation   108
   8.4 Effect of water on dynamic properties   109

9. Effect of Temperature and Pressure on Rock Properties   111

   9.1 Stress levels in the earth's crust   111
   9.2 Strength and elasticity   112
   9.3 Plastic flow under extreme conditions   116

10. Structural Features of Massive Rock   119

   10.1 Deformation and failure structures in the earth's crust 119
   10.2 Classification of rock structures   127
   10.3 Effect of failure structures on rock strength   128
   10.4 Influence of scale on rock properties   130

11. Reinforcement of Massive Rock   133

   11.1 Flow reduction by stress relief   133
   11.2 Rockbolt reinforcement   135
   11.3 Rock stabilization by grouting   138

12. Measurement of Stress and Strain in Massive Rock   140

   12.1 *Mechanics of stress measurement*   141
   12.2 *Direct strain measurement*   142
   12.3 *Borehole strain measurement*   144
   12.4 *Absolute stress related to rock properties*   147
   12.5 *Indirect stress measurement*   149

13. Design in Rock   155

   13.1 *Classification of design criteria*   155
   13.2 *Mathematical analysis*   160
   13.3 *Model analysis*   163

Selected Bibliography   169

References   171

Index   177

Preface

In this book, I have attempted to present a simple, concise and reasonably comprehensive introduction to some of the theoretical and empirical criteria which may be used to define rock as a structural material.

The book is intended primarily for civil and mining engineers familiar with the processes of design and construction in rock, but less familiar with specific design criteria, and for students of engineering, geology and engineering geology requiring a more basic introduction to rock engineering than that of the more polygenous reviews available under the general heading of 'Rock Mechanics'.

The scope of the book is indicated by the contents. It sets out initially to examine, on the basis of idealized test conditions, the physical, elastic and rheological properties of rocks, their mode of failure and their reactions to dynamic loading, going on to show how these are affected by the environmental conditions and massive structural features associated with natural rock, and finally outlining some of the techniques by which this information may be used in the ultimate processes of design.

I am grateful to the following for advice, help or encouragement at various stages during the preparation of the book: P. B. Attewell, P. J. Farmer, R. A. Gayer, P. Protopapadakis, A. Roberts and J. Sinclair.

I. W. F.

Nomenclature

The symbols used in the text are, in most cases, those conventionally used in engineering terminology, with occasional variations for convenience.

The Units used are metric throughout the text and are quoted in terms of mass rather than force. This may be questioned both by the engineer and the scientist, since the English-speaking engineer invariably works in English units, whilst the scientist works in metric force units.

The decision to use a metric (mass) system was motivated partly by the belief that in the future this system will be used by the majority of ground engineers and partly because of its obvious simplicity. It is easily interchangeable with the English system:

$$\text{e.g.} \quad 1 \text{ ton/sq. ft} \simeq 1 \text{ kg/cm}^2 \simeq 1 \text{ atmosphere} \simeq 15 \text{ lb/sq. in.}$$
$$1 \text{ ft} \qquad = 0 \cdot 305 \text{ m}$$
$$1 \text{ lb} \qquad = 0 \cdot 454 \text{ kg}$$

In the theoretical treatment of elasticity, viscosity and rheology, where materials are subject to stress, it is conventional to quote tensile stress as a positive quantity and compressive stress as a negative quantity. Problems of engineering design in rock, however, are concerned with compressive stresses in the majority of cases. For convenience, therefore, the convention is reversed in the text, *compressive* stress being taken as *positive* and *tensile* stress as *negative*.

Introduction

The purpose of engineering design is the production of a physical structure capable of withstanding the environmental conditions to which it may be subjected. Many factors affect the design process, from dimension to risk and cost, but basically the ultimate design is a reflection of the properties of the structural material, and in particular its *mechanical properties* which define the characteristic reaction of the material to the force field of its environment.

There is therefore a fundamental two-stage process in any design operation: firstly, the force field acting on the structural material must be defined, and secondly, the reaction of the material to that force field must be determined. The first stage involves an analysis of the stresses acting within the structural members; the second involves a knowledge of the properties of the structural material. The more comprehensive this knowledge, the more exact will be the design and the more perfect will be the structure.

It is unfortunate that whilst there is adequate information available on the properties of most common structural materials, in the field of rock engineering a general lack of knowledge of material properties sometimes hinders correct design practice. This is due to several factors, the most important no doubt being the relative simplicity of design and high acceptance of risk in many rock engineering applications. Under such circumstances recorded case history and personal experience can assume high importance – often to the exclusion of more rational approaches. A further difficulty lies in the variability of rock properties – often within apparently similar rocks, and in the problem of defining satisfactorily for engineering purposes the exact nature of a rock as distinct from a soil.

The most common structures which the engineer may be required to design in rock may be divided into three classes, namely foundations and anchorages, slopes, and underground excavations including tunnels, shafts and mine workings. Of these, the only structures which might be considered complicated – mine workings – have the shortest life and the highest risk acceptance, whilst those with low risk acceptance – foundations, shafts and tunnels – involve simple design at relatively low stress levels. Nevertheless there have, in the recent past, been spectacular disasters associated with each class of structure (see Jaeger, 1963; Mencl, 1966; Bryan *et al.*, 1964) pointing to the need for a more positive approach to design in rock.

Such an approach necessitates initially a satisfactory definition of the term *rock* – a general geological term which includes all naturally occurring mineral aggregates. From the point of view of engineering terminology, a rock may be simply defined as a *competent* naturally occurring material as distinct from a *soil*, which may be defined as an *incompetent* naturally occurring material. In this context *competence* may be taken to refer to the relative *cohesion* of the water-saturated rock under zero-confining stress conditions. Obviously if a rock is loaded beyond its failure point it will cease to be competent and similarly a soil under confinement will gain in competence.

Such a criterion for rocks would eliminate all loose soils and most clays which are plastic in a naturally occurring state and must be treated separately. It must also exclude concretes and other artificial aggregates. The weakest 'rock' will therefore be some form of stratified shale.

The dividing line between rock and soil is, however, purely arbitrary, and where there is any doubt, it is preferable to consider the material as a soil and to design on that basis.

Having defined a rock, the next stage must be to classify its mechanical properties in such a way as to readily assist the professional engineer: this in essence is the purpose of the following text. The requirements of any proposed classification can best be understood by considering the approach of engineers designing in rock. At present the practical engineer (viz. Krynine and Judd, 1957; Reynolds, 1961) bases design primarily on experience and case history, whilst the academic engineer (Salomon, 1964; Coates, 1965; Obert and Duvall, 1967) bases his design on an assumption of rock as a brittle elastic solid, adjusting the design to take account of anelastic features in the rock.

This latter approach is rational, but limited by the assumed elasticity of the rock to the more competent rocks whose properties approach most nearly those of an elastic material. Where time-dependent effects are significantly large, introducing large-scale flow at sub-failure stresses over a given time period, it is obviously wrong to design a structure on the basis of brittle failure. In this case the design must be concentrated either on reducing the stresses around the structure to such an extent that flow is reduced to acceptable levels, or on designing a satisfactory support framework for the structure.

A factor of paramount importance in design in rock therefore is whether the rock will flow to a significant extent under given loading conditions. Only when this question is answered satisfactorily can conventional structural design based on sub-failure stresses be attempted.

A further important consideration in any analysis of rock properties is the question of environment. In most aspects of engineering design the structural material can be obtained in a specified state, both as regards internal structure and external or internal stress. Rock being a natural material must be accepted in its natural state, although this can be altered within limits by various forms of treatment such as bolting or grouting. This means that a rock or rock mass may often contain large quantities of water and various tectonic discontinuities, and may be subject to high confining pressures – all of which may radically alter its properties which are normally based on small-scale laboratory tests.

The rate of application of stress can also affect rock mechanical properties – in common with other structural materials; and since explosives are widely used in construction in rock, the propagation of dynamic stresses from an explosive source and the resistance of rock to these stresses – often exceeding by an order of magnitude its resistance to static stresses – must be considered.

In this book an attempt is made to deal comprehensively with all factors affecting rock properties. Where these can be treated mathematically an attempt is made to introduce theoretical concepts. Where this is impossible, an empirical and logical treatment is introduced which may jar the mathematical mind – the reasoning being that it is better to arrive rhetorically at a 10% error than theoretically at a 50% error; such is the nature of rock.

I

Chemical and Physical Rock Properties

Before discussing the specific mechanical properties of rocks, it is necessary to define a rock and discuss some of its chemical and physical properties – particularly its structure, which may assist or resist the application of design criteria. A rock, unlike a steel which can be refined to consistent internal state before use, is a naturally occurring material and must be used in its natural state. Certain simplifying assumptions are justified to assist design processes; others are not, and to a large extent the basis for all assumptions lies in the composition and structure of the rock.

1.1 Composition of Rocks

All rocks consist of an aggregate of mineral particles. The proportion of each mineral in the rock, together with the granular structure, the text ture and the origin of the rock serves as a basis for geological classification.

A *mineral* may be defined as an inorganic substance with consisten physical properties and a fixed chemical composition. With the exception of some carbon forms, sulphur and a few metals, all minerals are chemical compounds, each containing two or more elements in fixed proportions by weight. Some elements are present in many minerals, the commonest being oxygen and silicon, whilst others, including most of the precious and base metals, form an insignificant proportion of the rocks in the earth's crust.

The way in which the composition of the earth's crust is dominated by eight elements is shown in Table 1.1. These elements comprise approximately 98% of the earth's crust and together with other elements form twelve common minerals (Table 1.2) which make up 99% of all rocks in the earth's crust. The remainder of the known rock-forming minerals, numbering over 1,000, make up less than 1% of the earth's crust. It can be assumed, therefore, that most if not all rocks encountered in problems connected with mining or engineering work, will consist of two or more of these minerals, each of which has a particular set of physical properties which may affect the engineering properties of the

TABLE I.I

Elements in the Earth's crust		Approximate Proportion (%)
Oxygen	(O)	46·7
Silicon	(Si)	27·7
Aluminium	(Al)	8·1
Iron	(Fe)	5·0
Calcium	(Ca)	3·6
Sodium	(Na)	2·8
Potassium	(K)	2·6
Magnesium	(Mg)	2·1
		98·6

rock as a whole. In general though, mineral particles in a rock will be so small that under normal circumstances they can have little individual effect on the rock properties.

TABLE I.2   Common Rock-forming Minerals

Felspars	
Orthoclase	$KAlSi_3O_8$
Plagioclase	$\left\{\begin{array}{l}NaAlSi_3O_8\\CaAl_2Si_2O_8\end{array}\right\}$ variable
Quartz	SiO_2
Micas	
Muscovite	$KAl_2(Si_3Al)O_{10}(OH)_2$
Biotite	$K_2(MgFe)_6(SiAl)_8O_{20}(OH)_4$
Amphiboles	
Hornblende	Na, Ca, Mg, Fe, Al Silicate
Pyroxenes	
Augite	Ca, Mg, Fe, Al Silicate
Olivine	$(MgFe)_2SiO_4$
Calcite	$CaCO_3$
Dolomite	$CaMg(CO_3)_2$
Kaolinite	$Al_2Si_2O_5(OH)_4$
Iron oxides	Fe_2O_3
	$2Fe_2O_3, 3H_2O$

Properties such as the preferred direction of cleavage and fracture, hardness and crystal structure used to define minerals can, however, under certain circumstances determine the reaction of a rock to outside forces, particularly where large amounts of a relatively soft mineral with

TABLE I.3   Properties of Common Rock-forming Minerals

Mineral	Hardness (Moh Scale *1-10*)	Specific Gravity	Fracture	Structure
Orthoclase	6	2·6	Good cleavage at right angles	Monoclinic. Commonly occurs as crystals
Plagioclase	6	2·7	Cleavage nearly at right angles – very marked	Triclinic. Showing distinct cleavage lamellae
Quartz	7	2·65	No cleavage. Choncoidal fracture	Hexagonal
Muscovite	2·5	2·8	Perfect single cleavage into thin easily separated plates	Monoclinic. Exhibiting strong cleavage lamellae
Biotite	3	3		
Hornblende	5–6	3·05	Good cleavage at 120°	Hexagonal – normally in elongated prisms
Augite	5–6	3·05	Cleavage nearly at right angles	Monoclinic
Olivine	6–7	3·5	No cleavage	No distinctive structure
Calcite	3	2·7	Three perfect cleavages. Rhomboids formed	Hexagonal
Dolomite	4	2·8	Three perfect cleavages	Hexagonal
Kaolinite	1	2·6	No cleavage	No distinctive structure (altered felspar)
Haematite	6	5	No cleavage	Hexagonal

marked fracture properties, such as a mica or calcite, or of a particularly hard mineral, such as quartz, are present. Some mineral properties relevant to an analysis of the mechanical properties of rock are listed in Table 1.3. The Moh scale of hardness used in the table is based solely on the empirical property of one mineral to scratch another and rises from the softest, talc equivalent to unity to the hardest, diamond equivalent to 10. It is, as such, a useful scale for gauging the apparent toughness of a mineral. A more accurate and useful method of quoting hardness in terms of *sclerometer units* based on one of the pendulum sclerometer tests is sometimes used. The correlation between scratch hardness and sclerometer hardness is reasonably consistent (Figure 1.1) (Terichow and Larson, 1967).

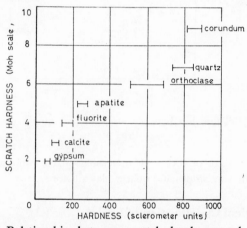

Figure 1.1 Relationship between scratch hardness and sclerometer hardness. (After Terichow and Larson.)

Hardness is sometimes used as a strength criterion in rocks, and as such it has a certain facile usefulness. It can, however, be shown that hardness/toughness parameters are related primarily to dynamic strength (Chapter 6) rather than to static strength – a factor which can lead to serious discrepancies in some rocks. For instance a fibrous rock, such as gypsum or anhydrite, may have a relatively low hardness but a high bulk strength. Accurate strength criteria for rocks will be developed in a later chapter, but it can immediately be seen that the anhydrous silicates (felspar, quartz, hornblende, augite, olivine) are considerably harder and hence stronger than any of the other common minerals except haematite. This is reflected to a certain extent in the mechanical properties of a rock – even where the rock contains only a

B

limited amount of the mineral. Price (1960, 1966) has related quartz content and uniaxial compressive strength (see Chapter 5) for a number of sandstones with calcite matrices and siltstones with predominantly clay mineral matrices. His results (Figure 1.2) demonstrate strikingly the

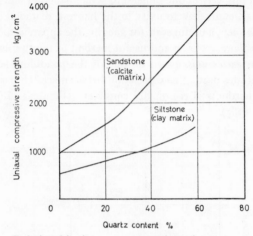

Figure 1.2   Relationship between strength and quartz content. (After Price.)

increasing strength of rock with increasing quartz content for typical quartz/calcite sandstones and quartz/clay siltstones.

1.2 Geological Classification of Rocks

TABLE 1.4   Geological Classification of Igneous Rocks

Texture	Acid > 66% Silica	Intermediate 52–66% Silica		Basic < 52% Silica	
PLUTONIC (coarse)	Granite	Syenite	Diorite	Gabbro	
HYPABYSSAL	Micro-Granite	—	—	Dolerite	Peridotite
VOLCANIC (fine)	Rhyolite Obsidian	Trachyte	Andesite	Basalt	Basalt
Major Mineral Constituents	Quartz Orthoclase (Mica)	Orthoclase Plagioclase (Mica)	Plagioclase Hornblende Orthoclase	Augite Plagioclase	Augite Hornblende Olivine

It is convenient to divide the rocks in the earth's crust into three different types based on their origin, namely igneous, sedimentary and metamorphic rocks. *Igneous* rocks are those formed by the solidification of molten magma, either at depth in the earth's crust or by extrusion – hence their classification as plutonic, hypabyssal, or volcanic, depending on the depth and rate of their cooling with its effect on their texture or

TABLE 1.5 Sedimentary Rock Classification

Method of Formation	Classification	Rock	Description	Major Mineral Constituents
MECHANICAL	Rudaceous	Breccia Conglomerate	Large grains in clay matrix	Various
	Arenaceous	Sandstone	Medium round grains in calcite matrix	Quartz, Calcite (sometimes Felspar, Mica)
		Quartzite	Medium round grains in silica matrix	Quartz
		Gritstone	Medium angular grains in matrix	Quartz,Calcite, various
		Breccia	Coarse angular grains in matrix	
	Argillaceous	Clay	Micro-fine grained – plastic texture	Kaolinite, Quartz, Mica
		Shale Mudstone	Harder – laminated Compacted clay	
ORGANIC	Calcareous	Limestone	Fossiliferous, coarse or fine grained	Calcite
	Carbonaceous (Siliceous ferruginous phosphatic)	Coal		
CHEMICAL	Ferruginous	Ironstone	Impregnated limestone or clay (or precipitated)	Calcite, Iron Oxide
	Calcareous (Siliceous, saline)	Dolomitic limestone	Precipitated or replaced limestone, fine grained	Dolomite, Calcite

crystal size. Igneous rocks are also subdivided by their composition into acid, intermediate and basic rocks, depending on the amount of silica in their composition. A full classification is given in Table 1.4. An immediate observation is the relative hardness of the mineral constituents of all igneous rocks. The mica content tends to be small.

Sedimentary rocks, the second major type, are those rocks formed by the deposition (usually under water) of products largely formed by the destruction of pre-existing igneous rocks. They tend to be weaker than igneous rocks, largely because of the hydration of felspars to form kaolinite and the introduction of organic minerals such as calcite. Sedimentary rocks can be subdivided into three main groups according to their method of formation, namely those mechanically formed, those formed from organic remains and those chemically deposited (see Table 1.5). From an engineering point of view, the most important are arenaceous (sand) rocks, argillaceous (clay) rocks and calcareous (limestone) rocks. Typical arenaceous rocks consist of discrete fragments of mineral – usually quartz, held together by a matrix of calcite. Thus when a sandstone is broken, the fracture follows the weaker calcareous cement rather than cutting across the stronger grains. An argillaceous rock such as a clay or shale consists of minute particles held together weakly and comprising largely kaolinite. The calcareous rocks consist of organic remains or precipitates,mainly in the form of calcite (limestone).

Metamorphic rocks may be either igneous or sedimentary rocks which have been altered physically and sometimes chemically by the application of intense heat or pressure at some time in their geological history. They are classified by their physical structure, i.e. massive or foliated (Table 1.6).

TABLE 1.6   Metamorphic Rock Classification

Classification	Rock	Description	Major Mineral Constituents
Massive	Hornfels	Micro-fine grained	Quartz
	Quartzite	Fine grained	Quartz
	Marble	Fine to coarse grained	Calcite or Dolomite
Foliated	Slate	Micro-fine grained, laminated	Kaolinite, Mica
	Phyllite	Soft, laminated	Mica, Kaolinite
	Schist	Altered hypabyssal rocks, coarse grained	Felspar, Quartz, Mica,
	Gneiss	Altered granite	Hornblende

It has been estimated that the earth's crust is made up of 95% igneous rocks, 5% sedimentary rocks and an insignificant proportion of metamorphic rocks. This does not, however, give a completely true picture of the rocks likely to be encountered by engineers working in rock. The earth's crust may be assumed to be from 30 to 50 km in thickness and virtually all major works take place in the top few kilometres which contain the major part of the sedimentary rocks. This means that the engineer working on the earth's surface or in near-surface mineral deposits (particularly in the United Kingdom) must contend with rocks which are often sedimentary, and also with some metamorphosed rock. In addition, a high percentage of these sedimentary rocks will be argillaceous, the majority of the remainder being arenaceous or calcareous.

This is in some ways unfortunate, since igneous rocks are with few exceptions competent, massive and strong while sedimentary rocks are weak and strongly foliated and jointed. Of the sedimentary rocks, the arenaceous and calcareous, under favourable conditions, approach nearest to the ideal of the igneous rocks. The argillaceous rocks depart furthest from them.

Argillaceous rocks comprise mainly shales, normally closely bedded or laminated, of two types; consolidated and cemented. The former are reasonably strong in a dry state, but weak when wet; the latter tend to have intermediate strength under most conditions, but are easily deformed under load. The problems encountered in mining, tunnelling or foundation work in such a rock are immediately apparent.

1.3 Rock Structure

It has been shown in the earlier sections that rocks are basically an aggregate of mineral particles. Many of the engineering properties of rocks to be discussed in later sections depend on the structure of these particles and the way in which they are bonded together.

In materials science there are two accepted types of structural unit from which all solid bodies are formed – namely crystals and molecules. The minerals which represent the basic rock structure normally take the form of crystals, but may exist as amorphous molecule aggregates (viz. silica). Crystals and molecules are formed from atoms – a *crystal* when the atoms are arranged in a stable three-dimensional pattern made up of units which are repeated indefinitely in all dimensions. The *molecule*, on the other hand, is defined as the smallest particle retaining the essential properties of the whole and when in the role of the basic structural unit forms an *amorphous* mass held together by intermolecular bonds. This can be demonstrated most clearly by considering the crystalline and amorphous forms of silica (Figure 1.3). In the crystal

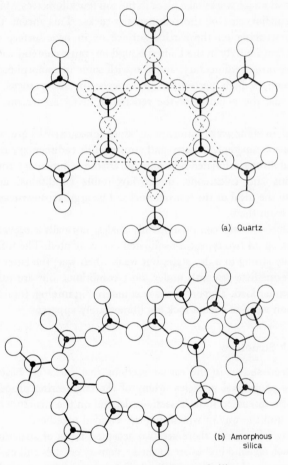

(a) Quartz

(b) Amorphous silica

Figure 1.3 Structural forms of silica.

form (quartz) there is a regular crystal lattice, made up of units, each comprising silicon atoms bonded to four oxygen atoms and oxygen atoms bonded to two silicon atoms. In the amorphous form the bonds are similar but the structural pattern is destroyed.

In nature few minerals exist in pure macro-crystal form and few in a purely amorphous form. Normally a mineral particle in a rock will consist of an aggregate of micro-crystals, held together by some form of ionic, atomic or molecular bonding. In the rock these mineral particles are cemented together by a matrix or by mechanical bonding at contact interfaces between the grains. Thus the ultimate strength of the rock will depend primarily on the strength of the matrix and the contact area between the grains; which since the matrix is also a polycrystalline aggregate, means that strength (other factors remaining constant) will be proportional to contact area and inversely proportional to grain size. The behaviour of the rock will also be affected by imperfections in the structure such as voids (pore space), cracks, inclusions, grain boundaries and weak particles. The granular structure of four common rocks is illustrated in Figure 1.4.

In terms of mechanical strength, *basalt* is one of the most competent of common rocks. Formed by volcanic action, it has a micro-fine texture and consists of micro-crystals of augite and plagioclase held together by strong mechanical bonding. A feature of basalt and other extrusive igneous rocks which may sometimes reduce its strength is the presence of voids (amygdoloids) formed by trapped gases unable to escape during its rapid cooling.

Granite is also strong, but its coarse texture and the presence of large crystals of orthoclase in particular, tend to make it substantially weaker than the fine-grained igneous rocks, and more comparable with the harder sandstones. Granite is formed by plutonic cooling of magma and, in these conditions, the orthoclase felspar, with a rather higher melting point than the other major constituent, quartz, tends to crystallize out surrounded by polycrystalline quartz. In other words, the sedimentary structure of mineral particles in a matrix is simulated, and the strength of the granite depends to a certain extent on the presence of other minerals such as mica tending to weaken the 'matrix'. There is a marked absence of voids.

Sandstone is a typical sedimentary rock consisting of rounded quartz particles cemented together by a calcite, ferruginous or silica matrix. The strength depends mainly on the strength of the matrix and the type and amount of pore space on it. A sedimentary quartzite (silica matrix) will be stronger than granite. A large-grain calcareous sandstone weakly cemented with a high proportion of non-contact void spaces will be extremely weak. The grain size (normally 1–0·1 mm) will also affect the amount of pore space.

Shale (mudstone) is a compressed clay consisting of micro-fine particles of kaolin, mica and quartz, normally in the micron range. A cemented shale can approximate in character to a concrete or weak sandstone. Shales differ from clays in that compaction gives the clay

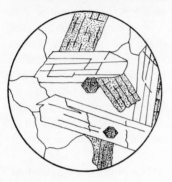

(a) Granite X 15

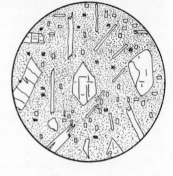

(b) Basalt X 15

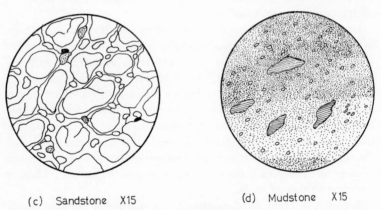

(c) Sandstone X 15   (d) Mudstone X 15

Figure 1.4 Rocks in section.

material a certain molecular cohesion which is not entirely lost under wet conditions. A clay, on the other hand, loses all strength when wet, failure depending solely on density and load; similar effects may occur in compacted shales where mechanical disturbance may lead to reversion, but here failure is normally due to the laminated structure of the rock and the presence of 'slippery' minerals such as kaolinite.

The weakness of shales is primarily due to their relative lack of compaction and hence high pore space. If subject to higher pressures this can be reduced, with consequent increase in strength, in the form of mudstones and eventually slates. The presence of large proportions of fine-grain quartz (silt-stone) will also increase strength.

1.4 Pore Space in Rock

Of all the physical characteristics of a rock which affect its mechanical properties, the most important is the presence of voids or pore spaces. All polycrystalline materials are porous and rocks, representing the weakest type of polycrystalline substance, are comparatively very porous – the amount of porosity depending on the type and structure of the rock. Pore spaces are largely made up of continuous irregular capillary cracks separating the mineral grains; the degree of porosity depending to a large extent on the method of formation of the rock. Thus in the case of igneous rock a slowly cooling magma will render a relatively non-porous rock, whereas a rapidly cooling lava particularly associated with escaping gases will yield a porous rock. In the case of

TABLE 1.7   Porosity and Density of Rocks

Rock	Bulk Density (gm/cc)	Porosity (%)
Granite	2·6–2·7	0·5–1·5
Dolerite	3·0–3·05	0·1–0·5
Rhyolite	2·4–2·6	4 –6
Andesite	2·2–2·3	10 –15
Gabbro	3·0–3·1	0·1–0·2
Basalt	2·8–2·9	0·1–1·0
Sandstone	2·0–2·6	5 –25
Shale	2·0–2·4	10 –30
Limestone	2·2–2·6	5 –20
Dolomite	2·5–2·6	1 –5
Gneiss	2·9–3·0	0·5–1·5
Marble	2·6–2·7	0·5–2
Quartzite	2·65	0·1–0·5
Slate	2·6–2·7	0·1–0·5

Porosity $\quad n_a = \dfrac{(w_s - w_0)}{V} \cdot \rho w$

Density $\quad \rho = \dfrac{w_0}{V}$

where w_0, V are weight and volume of dry rock and w_s is the weight of saturated (water) rock.

sedimentary rocks porosity will depend largely on the amount of cementing materials present and the size, grading and packing of the granular constituents. Some typical values of porosity, expressed in terms of the percentage pore space in the rock, are given in Table 1.7.

It could be argued that the presence of pore space in a rock would affect to a large extent the density of the rock, for with the exception of hornblende and augite, most of the common rock-forming minerals have similar densities in the range 2·65–2·8 gm/cc. Certainly this would be the case with the majority of acid-igneous and sedimentary rocks, comprising primarily quartz, felspar, calcite and kaolinite, where the density (ρ) should be related to porosity in the approximate form $\rho = 2\cdot65/(1 + n_a)$ gm/cc. That this does not appear so in practice can only cast doubt on the validity of porosity tests on low-porosity materials.

This raises the interesting possibility of a relationship between density and mechanical properties. If a rock has internal space its cohesion – molecular or mechanical – will obviously be affected by the amount of internal contact between its constituent fractions. This will be less in the case of a highly porous rock and this will be reflected particularly in the strength of the rock. The situation is represented in Figure 1.5, based on the observations of D'Andrea *et al.* (1965) and Judd and Huber (1962), and showing a clear curvilinear relationship between compressive strength and density. This is considered further in Chapter 5.

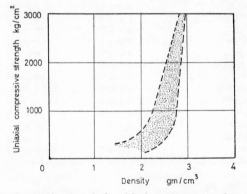

Figure 1.5   Approximate relationship between strength and density.

2

Stress and Strain

The mechanical properties of a rock are governed by the reaction of the rock to the forces acting upon it. These forces induce in the rock body a state of *stress*, a quantity with the dimension of force per unit area, and a state of *strain*, a dimensionless quantity expressing deformation in terms of the original dimension. The relationship between stress and strain in an idealized material forms the basis of the mathematical theories of elasticity, viscosity and rheology which can in turn be applied to actual materials (in this case rock) to estimate stress or strain in a specified force field.

An understanding of stress and strain and the principles of stress and strain analysis is therefore essential to the engineer designing structures in rock. These principles (see Timoshenko and Goodier, 1951; Jaeger, 1962) are developed briefly in the following chapter.

2.1 Stress at a Point

The stress at a point O in a solid body may be obtained by considering a plane at random orientation in the body and of small area δA (Figure 2.1a) which contains O. Then if δF is the resultant of all the forces exerted on A, the stress acting on O in a direction normal to the plane is defined as:

$$\mathbf{P_0} = \lim_{\delta A \to 0} \frac{\delta F}{\delta A} \tag{2.1}$$

where $\mathbf{P_0}$ is a vector quantity.

Thus for every point in the body a vector $\mathbf{P_0}$ exists defining the magnitude of the stress in every direction.

Since $\mathbf{P_0}$ is a vector quantity it can be represented by three components: a directional component and a normal and tangential stress component mutually at right angles or, if the orientation of the plane is known, by three stress components. In order that stress may be analysed easily, the plane on which it is acting can be related to a system of rectangular co-ordinates, x, y, z, where z is the vertical axis and x, y are mutually perpendicular horizontal axes. If δA is taken to lie in the YZ plane, the vector $\mathbf{P_0}$ can then be represented by the components (Figure 2.1b):

$$\sigma_x, \tau_{xy}, \tau_{xz} \qquad (2.2)$$

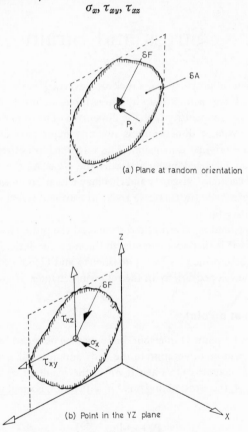

(a) Plane at random orientation

(b) Point in the YZ plane

Figure 2.1 Stress at a point in a plane.

where σ_x, normal to δA, is known as the *normal* stress component and τ_{xy}, τ_{xz} acting in the YZ plane are known as the tangential or *shear* stress components.

Similarly if the orientation of δA is such that it lies in the XZ plane, the normal and shear stress components at O will be:

$$\tau_{yx}, \sigma_y, \tau_{yz} \qquad (2.3)$$

and in the XY plane:

$$\tau_{zx}, \tau_{zy}, \sigma_z \qquad (2.4)$$

Thus the stress at point O can be represented fully in three dimensions by a total of nine components:

$$\begin{matrix} \sigma_x & \tau_{xy} & \tau_{xz} \\ \tau_{yx} & \sigma_y & \tau_{yz} \\ \tau_{zx} & \tau_{zy} & \sigma_z \end{matrix} \qquad (2.5)$$

which may be represented (Figure 2.2) as the forces acting on an elemental cube.

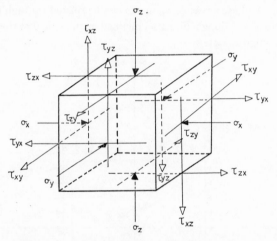

Figure 2.2 Representation of stress at a point.

In actual fact at a point in a body, constraint will impose rotational equilibrium, so that $\tau_{xy} = \tau_{yx}$, $\tau_{xz} = \tau_{zx}$ and $\tau_{yz} = \tau_{zy}$ and therefore only six stress components are needed to define the stress at a point in a body.

In all problems involving stress, the symbol σ is used to define normal stress and τ shear stress. In the case of shear stress the first suffix denotes the direction of the corresponding normal component, thus xy denotes a normal stress in the x-direction, and yx in the y-direction in the YZ and XZ planes respectively. In elastic theory, it is conventional to denote a tensile stress (elongation) as positive. In the present case, because rocks are normally subject to compression, it is convenient to reverse convention, taking a compressive stress as positive and a tensile stress as negative.

2.2 Combined Stress Analysis

Depending on the dimension of the loaded body a state of stress may be uniaxial, biaxial or triaxial. Since triaxial stress analysis may involve complicated three-dimensional geometry, fundamental theory is often based on an analysis of a two-dimensional or even a uni-dimensional approximation.

For instance if the stress at point O is considered two-dimensionally in the XZ plane, it can be assumed to include four stress components, σ_x, σ_z, τ_{xz}, τ_{zx}. (It must be remembered that the same plane will contain nine strain components in problems involving stress/strain relationships.) These stress components can be related through the stress acting across and along a direction inclined at an angle θ to the z-axis in the form (Figure 2.3):

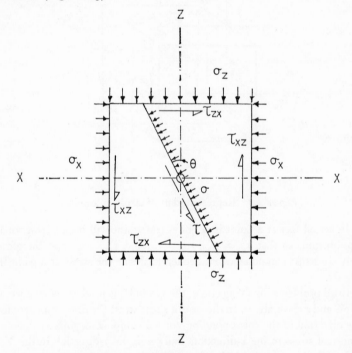

Figure 2.3   Combined stress in a plane.

$$\sigma = \sigma_x \cos^2 \theta + 2\tau_{xz} \sin \theta \cos \theta + \sigma_z \sin^2 \theta \tag{2.6}$$
$$\tau = (\sigma_z - \sigma_x) \sin \theta \cos \theta + \tau_{xz}(\cos^2 \theta - \sin^2 \theta) \tag{2.7}$$

(Since rotational equilibrium is maintained, $\tau_{xz} = \tau_{zx}$).

These equations give a complete picture of the variation of stress at O with direction, showing that both σ and τ are related to the angle θ. If σ is differentiated with respect to θ it can be shown that maximum and minimum values of normal stress occur when:

$$\tan 2\theta = \frac{2\tau_{xz}}{\sigma_z - \sigma_x} \qquad (2.8)$$

which solves to give two values of θ with a difference of 90°, which if substituted in eqn (2.6) give maximum and minimum values of σ and if substituted in eqn (2.7) give a value for τ of zero.

Equation (2.8) therefore defines two oblique axes at right angles to each other on which act maximum and minimum normal stress and zero shear stress. These axes are known as the *principal axes* of stress and the stresses along them are called the *principal stresses*. The principal stresses are denoted by the symbols σ_1, σ_2, where σ_1 is the greater. For convenience in rock stress problems compressive stresses are again taken as positive, and σ_1 is assumed to take a vertical or z-direction.

The effect of this analysis is to redefine the state of stress at a point in a plane in terms of the principal stresses and their orientation to the z-axis. Once this orientation is known it is convenient to use the principal axes as the axes of reference; thus if in eqns (2.6) and (2.7) σ_1 is substituted for σ_z and σ_2 for σ_x so that $\tau_{xz} = 0$, the normal and shear stress in the direction θ are given by:

$$\sigma = \frac{\sigma_1 + \sigma_2}{2} + \frac{\sigma_1 - \sigma_2}{2} \cos 2\theta \qquad (2.9)$$

$$\tau = \frac{\sigma_1 - \sigma_2}{2} \sin 2\theta \qquad (2.10)$$

There are various methods of representing the relationship between σ, τ and θ diagrammatically and of these the *Mohr circle construction* is the most elegant (Figure 2.4). This takes the form of a graph of shear stress against normal stress. On the normal stress axis, lengths are marked off to represent σ_1 and σ_2 and a circle, centre $(\sigma_1 + \sigma_2)/2$, radius $(\sigma_1 - \sigma_2)/2$ is constructed to pass through σ_1 and σ_2. Then the normal and shear stress in a direction θ to the major principal stress are given by the co-ordinates of A, the intersection between the circle and a diameter inclined at a clockwise angle 2θ to the normal stress axis. As would be expected, τ is a maximum where $\theta = 45°$, when it is equal to half the difference in the principal stresses and the equivalent normal stress is equal to half the sum of the principal stresses. The import-

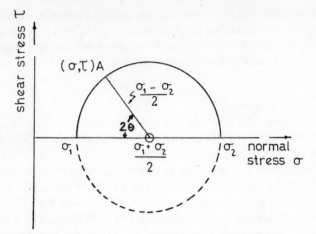

Figure 2.4 Mohr circle representation of stress.

ance of this will be seen in Chapter 5 when the tendency of rocks to fail in shear is discussed.

The analysis of stress at a point in a plane can be extended to include stress at a point in a three-dimensional solid where it can be shown from an analysis of the stress in the three planes defining the point, that the state of stress can be related to three principal stresses acting mutually at right angles. These are denoted by σ_1, σ_2, σ_3, where σ_1 is the largest (compressive) and σ_3 is the smallest principal stress. In such a system, it can readily be seen that except under conditions of hydrostatic loading ($\sigma_1 = \sigma_2 = \sigma_3$), there will be three planes of 'maximum' shear stress

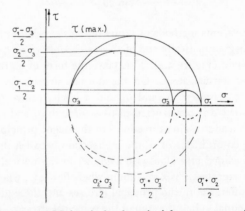

Figure 2.5 Mohr circles for triaxial stress at a point.

and three 'families' of planes on which shear stress can act at differing angles to the various axes. The total stress state can be represented by three Mohr circles on the shear/normal stress axes (Figure 2.5), each circle representing the stress state on a different plane. Then the maximum shear stress in each plane is respectively:

$$(\sigma_1 - \sigma_2)/2, \quad (\sigma_2 - \sigma_3)/2, \quad (\sigma_1 - \sigma_3)/2$$

of which the latter is the greatest. There is therefore in all three dimensional stress problems one plane of maximum shear stress occurring in the plane bounded by the directions of maximum and minimum principal stress. Thus if a material such as rock is known to fail in shear, it will obviously tend to fail in the plane of maximum shear, and it is relatively easy to define the likely direction and magnitude of failure from a knowledge of the state of stress at a point.

2.3 Strain at a Point

When a material is deformed, provided that the resultant displacement is small, *strain* may be defined as the displacement divided by the original dimension. Strain can be measured either as change in length (L) (extension or contraction), in which case it will be *normal* strain ε, or in terms of the angle of displacement (ψ) to give *shear* strain (γ) (Figure 2.6). Thus:

$$\varepsilon = \frac{\Delta L}{L} \quad \gamma = \tan \psi \tag{2.11}$$

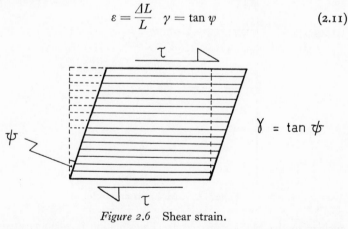

Figure 2.6 Shear strain.

Unlike the concept of uniaxial stress, it is difficult to envisage strain except as a biaxial or triaxial phenomenon, since lateral strains will always be induced by a normal strain. The simplest representation of

c

plane strain at a point follows closely the analysis of plane stress, defining normal and shear strain in an XZ plane with reference to a specified direction θ as:

$$\varepsilon = \varepsilon_x \cos^2 \theta + \gamma_{xz} \sin \theta \cos \theta + \varepsilon_z \sin^2 \theta \qquad (2.12)$$

$$\gamma = (\varepsilon_z - \varepsilon_x) \sin 2\theta + \gamma_{xz} \cos 2\theta \qquad (2.13)$$

These equations are directly comparable with eqns (2.6) and (2.7), and upon differentiation give a limiting value of θ where γ becomes zero when:

$$\tan 2\theta = \frac{\gamma_{xz}}{\varepsilon_z - \varepsilon_x} \qquad (2.14)$$

thus defining two *principal axes of strain*, the directions in which shear strain is zero and in which the normal strains may be accounted *principal strains*, ε_1 and ε_2. Then putting $\varepsilon_z = \varepsilon_1$ and $\varepsilon_x = \varepsilon_2$ and making $\gamma_{xz} = 0$, the normal and shear strain in a direction θ to the maximum principal strain are given by:

$$\varepsilon = \frac{\varepsilon_1 + \varepsilon_2}{2} + \frac{\varepsilon_1 - \varepsilon_2}{2} \cos 2\theta \qquad (2.15)$$

$$\gamma = (\varepsilon_1 - \varepsilon_2) \sin 2\theta \qquad (2.16)$$

which may be represented on the *Mohr strain circle* (Figure 2.7), a direct

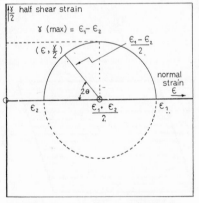

Figure 2.7   Mohr strain circle.

analogy to the Mohr stress circle. The notation is again positive for compression. This tends to appear strange since most strain – even in rock strain measurements – is measured in terms of elongation, by relief techniques. However, the major principal strain (in the direction of the major principal stress) must represent a contraction, if the stress is compressive.

Equations (2.15) and (2.16) can be used to determine experimentally the principal strains and their directions on the surface of a strained solid by the use of *strain gauges* (see Chapter 12) in a rosette form in three directions. If three strain gauges are placed at angles of $45°$ to each other in three directions A, B and C, then if ε_A, ε_B, ε_C are the measured strains in each direction it can be shown that:

$$\left.\begin{array}{l} \varepsilon_1 + \varepsilon_2 = \varepsilon_A + \varepsilon_C \\[6pt] \varepsilon_1 - \varepsilon_2 = [(\varepsilon_A - 2\varepsilon_B + \varepsilon_C)^2 + (\varepsilon_A - \varepsilon_C)^2]^{\frac{1}{2}} \\[6pt] \tan 2\theta = \dfrac{\varepsilon_A - 2\varepsilon_B + \varepsilon_C}{\varepsilon_A - \varepsilon_C} \end{array}\right\} \quad (2.17)$$

As with the case of stress, the theory of strain at a point may be developed in the three-dimensional case to show three principal axes of strain and three principal strains ε_1, ε_2, ε_3, acting at a point in a solid body.

2.4 Strain Ellipse

So far the only strain considered has been infinitesimal strain, a convention used in the theory of elasticity, since it is virtually impossible to treat the concept of finite strain mathematically in a simple form. This arises from the original concept of shear strain (Figure 2.6), which regards the angular displacement as due to the shearing or slip of straight lines or planes relative to one another. Obviously, except in the case of small displacements, the unstrained straight lines will tend to become curves on straining unless the state of strain at the point considered is the same throughout the whole body. If this assumption is made – and it may well be valid in small applications – then it is possible to define mathematically finite strain or more correctly finite homogeneous strain.

An analysis of finite strain can be obtained by considering the deformation of a circle in a plane where there is no rotation to form an ellipse, which will occur with any out of balance of deformation-inducing forces (Figure 2.8). Then in an XZ plane, the equation of the unstrained circle will be:

$$x^2 + z^2 = r^2 \qquad (2.18)$$

and of the strain ellipse:

$$\frac{x^2}{a^2} + \frac{z^2}{c^2} = 1 \qquad (2.19)$$

where a and c ($<a$) are the major and minor axes of the strain ellipse.

The intersection of the circle and the strain ellipse will give the equation and inclination (β) to the x-axis of the lines whose length is unchanged by straining, viz:

$$x^2\left(\frac{1}{a^2} - \frac{1}{r^2}\right) + z^2\left(\frac{1}{c^2} - \frac{1}{r^2}\right) = 0 \qquad (2.20)$$

$$\tan \beta = \pm\frac{c(a^2 - r^2)^{\frac{1}{2}}}{a(r^2 - c^2)^{\frac{1}{2}}} \qquad (2.21)$$

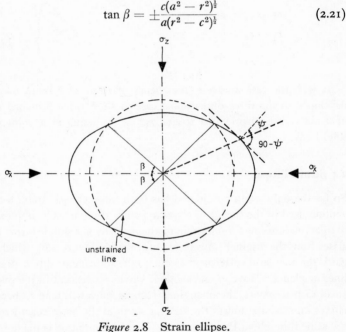

Figure 2.8   Strain ellipse.

The shear strain in any direction can be obtained from the angle between the radius vector and the tangent at a point on the ellipse, which is equal to $90 - \psi$, where $\tan \psi = \gamma$, giving a shear strain equal to:

$$\gamma = \tan \psi = \frac{(z/x)(a^2 - c^2)}{c^2 - a^2(z^2/x^2)} \qquad (2.22)$$

which has a maximum value, where $z/x = \pm(c/a)$, in which position:

$$\tan \beta = c/a \qquad (2.23)$$

giving the angle between the major axis of the ellipse and the directions of shear strain.

This analysis can be extended to three-dimensional strain by considering the deformation of a sphere $x^2 + y^2 + z^2 = 1$ into a strain ellipsoid

$$\frac{x^2}{a^2} + \frac{y^2}{b^2} + \frac{z^2}{c^2} = 1$$

giving an equation for planes of unchanged length analogous to eqn (2.20) in the form:

$$x^2\left(\frac{1}{a^2} - \frac{1}{r^2}\right) + y^2\left(\frac{1}{b^2} - \frac{1}{r^2}\right) + z^2\left(\frac{1}{c^2} - \frac{1}{r^2}\right) = 0 \qquad (2.24)$$

The intersection of planes of equal strain with the major axis can be found from the intersection of the strain ellipsoid and a sphere of diameter equal to the intermediate ellipsoid axis (b), giving two planes through the origin represented by:

$$x^2\left(\frac{1}{a^2} - \frac{1}{b^2}\right) + z^2\left(\frac{1}{c^2} - \frac{1}{b^2}\right) = 0 \qquad (2.25)$$

and inclined at an angle β to the x-axis, where:

$$\tan \beta = \pm\frac{c(a^2 - b^2)^{\frac{1}{2}}}{a(b^2 - c^2)^{\frac{1}{2}}} \qquad (2.26)$$

These planes and the planes parallel to them cut the ellipsoid in circular sections of equal strain.

Finite homogeneous strain can be represented graphically on a Mohr diagram analogous to the Mohr circles for stress and infinite strain by considering instead of strain, the quadratic compression or elongation (λ) of the material. In the directions of the principal axes of strain this is represented by:

$$\lambda_1 = (1 + \varepsilon_1)^2, \quad \lambda_2 = (1 + \varepsilon_2)^2, \quad \lambda_3 = (1 + \varepsilon_3)^2$$

where λ_1, λ_2, λ_3 are known as the *principal quadratic elongations or compressions* (the factor ε^2 is negligible in infinitesimal strain considerations).

It can be shown that λ is related to shear strain γ in the plane form:

$$\frac{(\lambda_1 + \lambda_2)^2}{4}\lambda_1\lambda_2\gamma^2 + \left[\lambda - \frac{(\lambda_1 - \lambda_2)}{2}\right]^2 \qquad (2.27)$$

which is an ellipse, which plotted on γ, λ axes has its centre at O, $(\lambda_1 + \lambda_2)/2$, a major axis in the λ direction of $(\lambda_1 - \lambda_2)/2$ and a minor axis in the γ direction of $(\lambda_1 - \lambda_2)/2\sqrt{(\lambda_1\lambda_2)}$. Similar ellipses represent the $\lambda_1\lambda_3$ and $\lambda_2\lambda_3$ planes in the three-dimensional case (Figure 2.9).

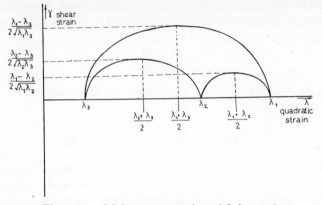

Figure 2.9   Mohr representation of finite strain.

From this, values of λ, γ in a direction θ in the plane of the major and minor principal strains are given by

$$\lambda = \frac{\lambda_1 + \lambda_3}{2} + \frac{\lambda_1 + \lambda_3}{2} \cos 2\theta$$

$$\gamma = \frac{\lambda_1 - \lambda_3}{2\sqrt{(\lambda_1 \lambda_2)}} \sin 2\theta$$

(2.28)

where γ has a maximum value where $\theta = 45°$, equivalent to β in eqn (2.23).

2.5 Stress/Strain Relationship

The analysis in the foregoing sections of stress and strain at a point holds for all materials, since each was treated independently and no relating conditions were introduced. However, since stress is in many ways a theoretical concept of internal load per unit area, there are few satisfactory methods of measuring it at a point in a body and it is normally necessary to measure the strains and relate these to stresses to obtain a satisfactory picture of stress distribution in a body. The stress/strain relationship for a material depends on many factors, including the homogeneity, isotropy and continuity of the body material, its reaction to loading over a period and the rate and magnitude of loading. Under certain conditions, such as would be presented by a highly anisotropic material, the difficulties involved in stress analysis can be virtually insuperable. If, however, the unit under load is large enough and the loading conditions are defined within certain limits, it is possible to assume that rocks under load can be treated as elastic, viscous or rheo-logical materials for the purposes of stress/strain analysis, thus pro-viding a direct stress/strain relationship, a strain/time, stress/time relationship or a combination of the two.

These relationships and their application to rocks are discussed in the following chapters.

3

Elastic Properties of Rocks

The simplest way of relating stress and strain is by direct linearity. This is the fundamental basis of elastic theory (Timoshenko and Goodier, 1951), which postulates an elastic medium in which all strain is instantaneously and totally recoverable on the removal of the stress. An elastic medium is an idealization of actual material properties, for obviously deformation involving structural adjustment inside the material will be a finite process even in materials approaching the ideal, and in materials which are less than ideal (including rocks) there will be less than total recovery. It is necessary therefore in considering the reaction of rocks under load to define initially their elasticity as compared with the ideal and to attempt to define the limitations of analysis by elastic theory.

3.1 Stress/Strain Relationship in an Elastic Medium

In an elastic medium stress is directly proportional to strain (Figure 3.1), and the two are related linearly in Hooke's law:

$$\sigma/\varepsilon = E \qquad (3.1)$$

where E is a constant known as the *modulus of elasticity* and represents in a mechanical sense the *stiffness* of the material.

Apart from a change in sign convention, there is no difference in the effects of compression or tension on the elastic deformation except that in compression (taken as positive), the limit of elastic deformation (ε_L) is considerably larger than in tension. Since in *brittle* materials this limit represents the fracture point or *strength* (S) of the material, it has considerable importance in the study of rocks.

Equation 3.1 represents deformation in a single direction. Hooke's law can also be adapted for hydrostatic and shear deformation in the forms:

$$\frac{\delta P}{\delta V} = K, \quad \frac{\tau}{\gamma} = G \qquad (3.2)$$

where δP is the unit change in hydrostatic pressure causing δV a unit change in volume.

K is the bulk modulus or compressibility, τ is the shear stress, γ is the shear strain, and G is the modulus of rigidity.

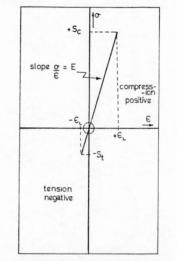

Figure 3.1   Elastic stress/strain relationship.

Another important parameter in elastic theory is *Poisson's ratio ν*, which represents the inverse ratio between strain in the direction of applied stress and induced deformation in a perpendicular direction. Thus

$$\nu = -\frac{\varepsilon_x}{\varepsilon_z} \qquad (3.3)$$

whence

$$\varepsilon_x = -\frac{\sigma_z}{E}\nu \qquad (3.4)$$

the negative sign representing an elongation. (ε_x and ε_z must be of different sign.)

An idealized value for Poisson's ratio can be obtained by considering an idealized crystal structure (Figure 3.2) with rows of atoms in a conventional lattice. Since they are bonded together, contraction in one direction will automatically lead to extension of the lattice in a perpendicular direction. In such a case the relationship between ε_z and ε_x can be obtained from the geometry of the deformation to show that $\nu = \frac{1}{3}$.

The relationship between direct and induced strain can also be

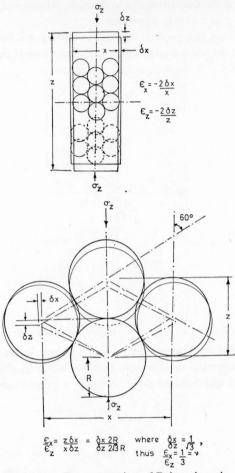

$$\frac{\varepsilon_x}{\varepsilon_z} = \frac{z\,\delta x}{x\,\delta z} = \frac{\delta x\,2R}{\delta z\,2\sqrt{3}\,R} \quad \text{where } \frac{\delta x}{\delta z} = \frac{1}{\sqrt{3}}, \\ \text{thus } \frac{\varepsilon_x}{\varepsilon_z} = \frac{1}{3} = \nu$$

Figure 3.2   Representation of Poisson's ratio.

expressed in terms of *Lamé's constant*, λ, and the modulus of rigidity, G, the shear stress/shear strain ratio, so that:

$$\frac{\varepsilon_x}{\varepsilon_z} = \frac{-\lambda}{2(\lambda + G)} = -\nu \qquad (3.5)$$

It can be shown that for most rocks λ and G have similar values, which if substituted in eqn (3.5) give a value for Poisson's ratio of 0·25, an interesting variation from the ideal.

If a material is isotropic (an assumption necessary in considering an elastic medium) the principal axes of stress and strain, defined separately in Chapter 2, must coincide, and the stress and strain at a point can be related by considering the total strain induced by each stress in each direction (eqns 3.3, 3.4).

For instance, consider an elemental cube subject to three compressive principal stresses σ_1, σ_2, σ_3. Then the principal strain in each direction assuming elasticity will be:

$$\varepsilon_1 = \frac{\sigma_1}{E} - \frac{v\sigma_2}{E} - \frac{v\sigma_3}{E} \qquad (3.6)$$

$$\varepsilon_2 = \frac{\sigma_2}{E} - \frac{v\sigma_1}{E} - \frac{v\sigma_3}{E} \qquad (3.7)$$

$$\varepsilon_3 = \frac{\sigma_3}{E} - \frac{v\sigma_1}{E} - \frac{v\sigma_2}{E} \qquad (3.8)$$

or in terms of G and λ in the form:

$$\varepsilon_1 = \frac{\sigma_1}{\lambda + 2G} - \frac{\sigma_2}{\lambda} - \frac{\sigma_3}{\lambda} \quad \text{etc.} \qquad (3.9)$$

Conversely the principal stresses may be obtained if the principal strains are known at a point and also two elastic constants, v and E or λ and G. These may be related to the fifth elastic constant K, by substituting for hydrostatic conditions, $\sigma_1 = \sigma_2 = \sigma_3 = \sigma$ in the above equations, whence:

$$\varepsilon = \frac{\sigma}{E}(1 - 2v) \qquad (3.10)$$

from which $\qquad K = \sigma\frac{V}{\delta V} \backsimeq \frac{\sigma}{3\varepsilon} = \frac{E}{3(1 - 2v)} \qquad (3.11)$

By a similar process E and G can be related in the form:

$$G = \frac{E}{2(1 + v)} \qquad (3.12)$$

3.2 Elasticity of Rocks

Elasticity is a property of an ideal material. It is a property of engineering materials, including rocks, to a greater or lesser extent, depending on how closely they approximate to the ideal. In practice, this depends on three major factors, *homogeneity*, *isotropy* and *continuity*, which may each be defined within certain limits.

Isotropy is a measure of the directional properties of a material. For instance, in a statistical sense, a granular body will be isotropic if all its grains have random orientation, and a plane of equal dimension intersecting the body in any direction exposes an equal number of grains.

Thus, since many rocks have a preferred particle and crystal orientation, they are strictly speaking anisotropic and would be expected to react differently to forces in different directions, depending on the degree of anisotropy.

Homogeneity is a measure of the physical continuity of a body. Thus in a homogeneous material, the constituents are distributed so that a minute fragment cut from any part of the body will have constituents and hence properties representative of the whole. Homogeneity is therefore largely dependent upon scale and it would be possible to describe a finely grained massive rock as homogeneous, whereas a large-grained rock with limited dimensions must be considered inhomogeneous.

Continuity can be taken to refer to the amount of joint, crack and pore space in a particular rock body. The degree of continuity will affect its cohesion and hence the transmission of even stress distribution throughout the body. The extremes in considering rock continuity would be a mass of fractured rock which is completely discontinuous and a massive body of fine-grained rock with hairline jointing which is nearly continuous.

From these definitions it is possible to arrive at a rough estimation of the likely elasticity of a rock, always remembering that with the possible exception of the extreme case of obsidian or a native metal, all rocks are to some extent anisotropic, inhomogeneous and discontinuous and are therefore less than perfectly elastic. Some rocks, however, do approximate in varying degrees some elastic properties, particularly under low deforming loads.

Obviously the most elastic rocks will be fine grained, massive and compact – a property of extrusive (except where aerated) and hypabyssal igneous rocks and some fine-grained metamorphic rocks. These rocks (Figure 3.3a) approximate in many ways the properties of a brittle elastic material having a near linear stress/strain relationship to the point of failure and can be termed *quasi-elastic* rocks.

Less elastic are coarser-grained igneous rocks and fine-grained compacted sediments, having low porosity and a reasonable amount of cohesion, termed *semi-elastic* rocks. These have a stress/strain relationship (Figure 3.3b) in which the slope of the curve (equivalent to the modulus of elasticity under defined loading conditions) decreases with increasing stress. This type of curve, obtained from tests on small laboratory specimens and therefore accentuating the inhomogeneity and anisotropy of the material, may in fact give an exaggerated picture of the anelasticity of this type of rock, which on a larger scale such as a massive deposit or bed may be amenable to elastic analysis. It illustrates one of the dangers of laboratory testing – even when coupled with statistical interpretation – as a method of obtaining data for large-scale analysis.

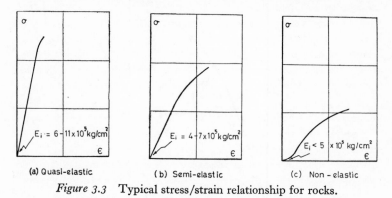

(a) Quasi-elastic   (b) Semi-elastic   (c) Non - elastic

Figure 3.3   Typical stress/strain relationship for rocks.

A similar danger exists in obtaining data for a third type of stress/strain relationship by laboratory methods. This category includes the less cohesive rocks with large pore space, comprising most of the weaker sedimentary rocks (Figure 3.3c). These are, however, self evidently *non-elastic*, and any analysis based on elasticity would be dangerous. The curve generally exhibits an initial zone of increasing slope with increasing load, a feature which intimates compaction and crack closure, before any near-linear deformation occurs. Such rocks tend to exhibit variable stress/strain characteristics.

The major features in the stress/strain relationship for a competent rock can be generalized in the form (Figure 3.4) of a curve with an approximate linear zone of maximum slope giving way to a curve of decreasing slope with increasing stress as the failure point is reached. The curve represents a rock in uniaxial compression (positive) – in tension the curve is similar in shape but failure occurs at a lower stress.

Although the curve may be taken to represent elastic type deformation of a rock, there remains a difficulty in obtaining a satisfactory value for the modulus of elasticity. This may be quoted in three ways, namely: (i) as the *secant* (E_s) modulus to a particular point, giving an average value of E below a specified stress limit, (ii) the tangent modulus (E_T) to a particular point on the curve, giving an apparent value of E at a specified stress, or (iii) the *initial* tangent modulus, (E_i), the slope of the line tangential to the curve and passing through the origin, giving the value of E under zero load – in effect the maximum value of E and sometimes taken as that obtaining under dynamic load conditions in unstressed rock.

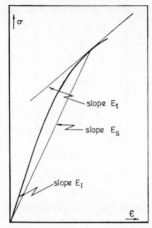

Figure 3.4 Generalized stress/strain curve for rock

The values of E obtained at any point on the curve can, for the average rock, be closely related (Judd and Huber, 1962) although their actual values may diverge by as much as 100%. For this reason the value of E quoted for a rock is normally the *initial tangent* modulus, since it is the most accurately obtained under test conditions. The tangent modulus at a particular load will then be from 100% to 50% of this value depending on the type of rock and the loading conditions, and the secant modulus to the point of failure from 90% to 50% of the initial tangent modulus, depending on the rock type.

Thus for a fine-grained near-elastic rock $E_s = E_T = 0.9E_i$, and for a coarse-grained anelastic rock $E_T = 0.9E_i$ for light static loads, $E_T = 0.8E_i$ for loads near to failure and $E_s = 0.5E_i$ at the failure point.

3.3 Elastic Constants for Rocks

To define any material elastically, two elastic constants are required from the five available (E, ν, K, G, λ). In elastic theory the most convenient are G, λ, but in engineering problems where a measure of the direct reaction of a rock to a force is required, E and ν are the most commonly quoted. However, in most quasi-elastic and semi-elastic rocks, all elastic constants can be related with a good degree of accuracy.

A list of values of E and ν are quoted in Table 3.1.

Based on a wide range of sources (including Hosking, 1955; Blair,

1955, 1956; Nicholls, 1961; Coates and Parsons, 1966; Windes, 1949, 1950) and on the author's own observations, these give the range of constants for a particular type of rock, the actual value depending largely on the cohesion of the rock. Thus a weak limestone would have a value for E in the region of 10^5 kg/cm^2, and a strong fine-grained limestone a value nearer to 10^6 kg/cm^2. It is possible to estimate, with experience, the modulus of elasticity of any rock by physical examination and simple empirical tests to within $\pm 20\%$ of its true value. This is sufficiently accurate for the majority of rock design calculations.

TABLE 3.1   Elastic Constants of Rocks at Zero Load

Rock	E (kg/cm^2)	ν
Granite	2–6 $\times$ 10^5	0·25
Microgranite	3–8 $\times$ 10^5	0·25
Syenite	6–8 $\times$ 10^5	0·25
Diorite	7–10 $\times$ 10^5	0·25
Dolerite	8–11 $\times$ 10^5	0·25
Gabbro	7–11 $\times$ 10^5	0·25
Basalt	6–10 $\times$ 10^5	0·25
Sandstone	0·5–8 $\times$ 10^5	
Shale	1–3·5 $\times$ 10^5	
Mudstone	2–5 $\times$ 10^5	
Limestone	1–8 $\times$ 10^5	
Dolomite	4–8·4 $\times$ 10^5	
Coal	1–2 $\times$ 10^5	

The three types of rock previously defined in terms of their relative anelasticity as *quasi-*, *semi-* and *non*-elastic can also be roughly delineated in terms of their apparent elastic moduli. Thus a quasi-elastic rock will have a value of E between 6 and 11 $\times$ 10^5 kg/cm^2, a semi-elastic rock between 4 and 7 $\times$ 10^5 kg/cm^2 and a non-elastic rock less than 5 $\times$ 10^5 kg/cm^2. The values quoted in each case are the initial tangent moduli.

The relationships between E and ν and other elastic constants and physical constants of rocks have been analysed statistically by Judd and Huber on the basis of the observations of Blair and Windes. They conclude that there is a direct linear relationship for all rocks tested between the modulus of elasticity and the modulus of rigidity and between the modulus of elasticity and the compressive strength of a rock. Any relationship between E and G, E and K, or λ and G would suggest that if rocks were elastic, then there should be a constant value of v for all rocks, irrespective of the magnitude of E. The graph relating E and v, reproduced in Figure 3.5, shows that whilst this ideal may be approached in rocks with a high modulus of elasticity, measured values of v for rocks with low moduli – which represent the non-elastic rocks – show

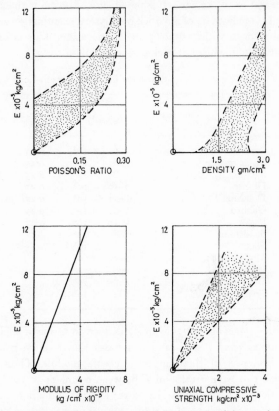

Figure 3.5 Relationship between modulus of elasticity and Poisson's ratio, density, modulus of rigidity and strength in rocks. (After Judd and Huber.)

variable and lower values of v. This evidence suggests that prediction of rock reactions in this type of rock should not be based wholly on elastic theory. It also suggests that physical measurement of v in the laboratory is less than wholly accurate.

Thus the stable linear relationship between G and E (Figure 3.5) in the approximate form, $E = 2 \cdot 5G$, suggesting a constant value of v equal to 0·25 (cf. eqns 3.5 and 3.12) must be seriously considered, since it may very well be that some of the discrepancies in the E/ν graph are due to erratic measurements of ν, which are rarely satisfactory in practice (see Chapter 7). Certainly in any work involving elastic analysis of rocks, there is sufficient evidence available to suggest that a value of 0·25 for Poisson's ratio should be assumed unless there is overwhelming evidence to the contrary. If this assumption cannot be made, then there are grounds for saying that the rock must be assumed anelastic, in which case the need for a Poisson's ratio value will cease.

The significance of the linear relationship between rock compressive strength (S_c) and the elastic moduli, taking the approximate form $E = 350S_c$, $G = 140S_c$, lies in the confirmation that rock strength is related to the stiffness (represented by E) and rigidity (represented by G) of the internal rock structure.

Other important trends suggested by Judd and Huber relate G and E in a near-linear form to the apparent rock density and in a curvilinear form to the longitudinal velocity of stress waves in the rock. The dynamic effects will be considered later, but the approximate relationship between E and the density has immediate importance. It can only lead to the conclusion that since most of the common rock-forming minerals have similar specific gravities, the elastic properties of a rock are affected to an overwhelming degree by the internal rock structure, represented especially by the grain size and degree of compaction and the subsequent presence of interior space in the rock. It must, however, be noted that there is no indication of a corresponding relationship between rock density and apparent porosity. This is surprising and must cast some doubt on the validity of the tests for apparent porosity as applied to rocks as distinct from 'soils'. Standard tests for apparent porosity, based on a highly porous soil saturated at atmospheric pressure over a short time period, are obviously unsuitable for rocks.

The apparent density (ρ) of a material may therefore be used as a basis to obtain an approximate value for E and hence for other rock constants by the rule-of-thumb formula:

$$E = 0·9(\rho - 2·1) \times 10^6 \, \text{kg/cm}^2 \qquad (3.13)$$

The accuracy of such values will fall in the range $\pm20\%$. This is not accurate and for an accurate design, experimentally obtained values of E from a large range of samples and sizes would be essential. However, many cases of design in rocks have included far greater inaccuracies in an initial assumption of elasticity for a particular rock. Thus before any analysis it is essential that initial assumptions be carefully checked.

D

3.4 Elastic Theory Applied to Design in Rock

A prerequisite in any design problem involving real materials is the assumption of certain simplifying material properties to assist mathematical analysis (Chapter 13). In problems involving design in rock this traditionally means an assumption of elastic properties for the rock, enabling calculations to be based on the theory of elasticity. Such designs have sometimes been successful; sometimes – particularly in cases involving rock slopes and foundations – they have introduced considerable degrees of error. It is therefore essential that the limits of applicability of elastic theory to rock be clearly defined.

It has been shown that, by the definition of elasticity, no rocks are truly elastic, but that some have deformational properties approximating to a *quasi-elastic* form, particularly some fine-grained cohesive rocks and massive rocks at low stress levels. Against this must be set the knowledge that rocks in nature are normally discontinuous containing various foliation surfaces, joints and associated cracks, and possibly faults and other failure structures, all of which may contain water in varying amounts. This aspect may be exacerbated in near-surface applications – often thought the optimum conditions for elastic analysis – where open joints and maximum water can lead to considerable error. On the other hand, at depth there will be a tendency for joints to be closed due to pressure, and for water to be absent, limiting the difference between sample and massive properties, although time-dependent flow will tend to increase with increasing load and temperature.

An actual decision on the limits of elasticity is therefore extremely difficult and must always be approached with caution, bearing in mind factors outside the normal internal structure of the rock. Generally, however, the following rules will give a useful guide:

(1) No near-surface rock structure should be treated as a continuous elastic medium however near-elastic its sample properties may be, unless it can be shown to contain a minimum of discontinuities. Design criteria must normally be based on friction at joint and bedding planes.

(2) No heavily jointed, bedded or fractured rock structure should be treated as continuous elastic medium.

(3) No rock with a measured modulus of elasticity less than 5×10^5 kg/cm² should be considered an elastic medium except with extreme caution.

(4) No rock under sufficient load to induce significant flow should be treated elastically.

4

Rheological Properties of Rocks

A perfectly elastic material exhibits instantaneous recovery when a deforming load below its elastic limit is removed. However, the deformation process in real materials tends to lag behind the stress application (Nadai, 1950, 1963) and engineering materials in general and rocks in particular are subject to reversible and irreversible time-dependent deformation when loaded over a finite time interval, even though the deforming stress may be well below the elastic limit of the rock. Thus a rock may be symbolized as deforming not only as an elastic solid, but also as a viscous fluid – although the time-dependent effects may be due to crushing of pore space or sliding on joint/bedding plane surfaces, rather than to any specific viscous property of the rock. Nevertheless it is possible to characterize time-dependent flow in rocks in terms of viscosity and to approach the analysis of stress in a rock in terms of fundamental rheological principles, despite the fact that rheology, like elasticity, is based on the concept of an ideal material.

Such an approach may be justified by comparing the actual time-dependent properties of a real material with an idealized rheological standard or model.

4.1 Rheological Models

The time-dependent properties of a material may be classified on the basis of observed reactions in the form of a series of rheological models made up of certain basic deformation elements represented by a spring (elastic deformation – *Hookean* substance), a dashpot (viscous deformation – *Newtonian* substance) and a frictional contact (plastic deformation above a yield point – *St Venant* substance). These imply respectively: (i) a linear relationship between stress and strain (eqn 3.1):

$$\sigma = E\varepsilon$$

(ii) a linear relationship between stress and rate of strain:

$$\sigma = \eta \frac{d\varepsilon}{dt} \qquad (4.1)$$

where η is the *coefficient of viscosity*,
and (iii) a constant rate of strain above a yield stress, represented by σ_L.

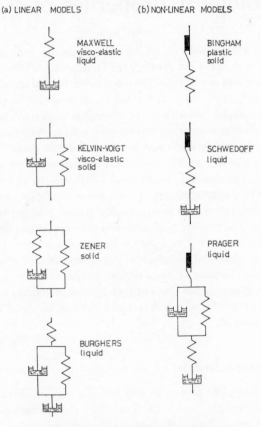

(a) LINEAR MODELS

MAXWELL
visco-elastic
liquid

KELVIN-VOIGT
visco-elastic
solid

ZENER
solid

BURGHERS
liquid

(b) NON-LINEAR MODELS

BINGHAM
plastic
solid

SCHWEDOFF
liquid

PRAGER
liquid

Figure 4.1   Rheological models.

These elements may be combined to form a series of 'linear' models
(Figure 4.1a) capable of linear equation, and 'non-linear' models
(Figure 4.1b) to describe the simpler forms of rheological deformation.
A typical example is the *Maxwell* model, consisting of a spring and dash-
pot in series and used to describe a perfectly visco-elastic (liquid)

material. The total normal strain (this could equally be shear deformation) of this model is given by the equation:

$$\varepsilon = \frac{\sigma}{E} + \frac{1}{\eta} \int \sigma \, dt \tag{4.2}$$

which can be expressed as a differential equation:

$$\frac{\sigma}{\eta} + \frac{1}{E} \frac{d\sigma}{dt} = \frac{d\varepsilon}{dt} \tag{4.3}$$

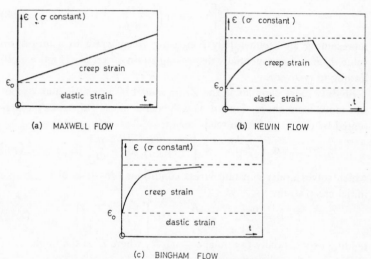

(a)   MAXWELL FLOW

(b)   KELVIN FLOW

(c)   BINGHAM FLOW

Figure 4.2 Typical creep strain representation.

The significance of this solution can be seen by considering conditions of constant stress ($d\sigma/dt = 0$) and constant strain ($d\varepsilon/dt = 0$). In the former case:

$$\frac{d\varepsilon}{dt} = \frac{\sigma_0}{\eta} \tag{4.4}$$

and the strain increases linearly with time (η is a measure of linear viscosity). This is what is known as *creep* (Figure 4.2a).

In the latter case:

$$\frac{\sigma}{\eta} + \frac{1}{E} \frac{d\sigma}{dt} = 0 \tag{4.5}$$

which solves to give the exponential form:

$$\sigma = \sigma_0 \exp\left(-\frac{Et}{\eta}\right) \tag{4.6}$$

demonstrating the exponential process of *stress relaxation* at constant strain, the corollary of creep.

Another example is the *Kelvin-Voight* model representing a visco-elastic (solid) substance and comprising a spring and dashpot in series, in which the stress/strain relationship takes the form:

$$\eta\frac{d\varepsilon}{dt} + \varepsilon E = \sigma \qquad (4.7)$$

which under constant stress (σ_0) conditions solves to give:

$$\varepsilon = \frac{\sigma_0}{E}\left[1 - \exp\left(-\frac{Et}{\eta}\right)\right] \qquad (4.8)$$

representing an exponentially increasing creep strain to a maximum value σ_0/E and exponentially decreasing strain on release (Figure 4.2b) leading to recovery.

Slightly more complex is the *Zener* model of an elastic and viscous substance, sometimes, known as a 'general linear substance', represented by the stress/strain relationship:

$$\sigma + \frac{\eta}{E}\frac{d\sigma}{dt} = E'\left[\varepsilon + \frac{\eta(E + E')}{EE'}\frac{d\varepsilon}{dt}\right] \qquad (4.9)$$

which solves under constant stress conditions ($d\sigma/dt = 0$) to give an initial creep strain:

$$\varepsilon = \frac{\sigma_0}{E'}\left\{1 - \frac{E}{E + E'}\exp\left[\frac{-EE't}{\eta(E + E')}\right]\right\} \qquad (4.10)$$

tending exponentially to a final $\varepsilon = \sigma_0/E'$, where E' is the modulus of elasticity of the solitary spring.

These three examples are all linear models. A simple example of a non-linear model, involving yielding, is the *Bingham/Schwedoff* substance. This represents an elastic body below the yield point, with an increasing creep strain for greater stresses (Figure 4.2c), viz.:

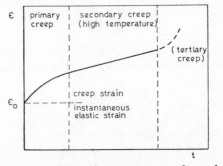

Figure 4.3 Generalized creep curve for rock.

$$\left.\begin{aligned} \sigma < \sigma_L, \quad \varepsilon &= \frac{\sigma}{E} \\ \sigma > \sigma_L, \quad \varepsilon &= (\sigma - \sigma_L)\frac{t}{\eta} + \frac{\sigma}{E} \end{aligned}\right\} \tag{4.11}$$

4.2 Flow in Rocks

In considering time-dependent deformation in rocks, consideration will be given initially to flow or creep as a uniaxial stress-induced phenomenon. This is based on the assumption that under normal engineering stress levels (as distinct from tectonic stress levels) flow or creep is not affected by the confining stress but only by the stress difference. This assumption which underlies most studies of creep in rock is difficult to justify, but without it, empirical or any other treatment of the complex phenomena involved becomes increasingly difficult. Conditions where confining pressures and other factors may substantially affect time-dependent deformation are considered in Chapter 9.

The time-dependent deformation of a rock subject to constant stress conditions can be generalized into four basic stages (Figure 4.3):

(a) Instantaneous elastic strain.

(b) Primary creep at a rapid but decelerating strain rate.

(c) Secondary creep at a low, or near constant strain rate, and either

(d) Possible tertiary creep accelerating to fracture.

or (e) Partial recovery of strain on release of the deforming stress.

Tertiary creep is not important. It is noted in fine-grain limestone by Griggs (1936) under hydrostatic stresses in the region of 6,000 kg/cm^2; far outside the normal range of rock stresses. In weaker rock (such as shale), where a considerable degree of flow would be expected, there is commensurately less tendency to failure. In any case, in a rock susceptible to creep, the amount of creep likely to precede failure will be so large that the actual failure point will cease to have major significance as a design factor.

An important feature of the creep curve is the recovery tendency following stress release. The amount of recovery varies with load and duration of stress, but is sufficient to suggest that creep in rocks may be best represented by a Kelvin-Voigt or Zener analogy, although the general form will fit most of the models itemized above, and it is likely that for exact representation of a particular rock, different and highly complex models will be required (see Kidybinski, 1966).

The Kelvin-Voigt/Zener analogy may be extended further by considering the empirical form of the creep curve (Figure 4.3) in its first two stages (a, b). This transient creep can be generally represented by two terms, corresponding to the elastic strain (stage a) and a variable time-dependent function (stage b), viz.:

$$\varepsilon = \varepsilon_0 + f(t) \qquad (4.12)$$

where $f(t)$ is a function whose derivative decreases with time, stress and temperature.

Temperature has a significant effect on creep, particularly at high levels, but is not significant in problems associated with design in rock, where a maximum temperature below $100\,°C$ can be assumed, in which case $f(t)$ may be equated to $A \log_e t$, where A is a coefficient depending on the magnitude of stress, and known as the *creep constant*. Equation (4.12) therefore becomes:

$$\varepsilon = \varepsilon_0 + A \log_e t \qquad (4.13)$$

This ignores a constant time function (i.e. *secondary* creep) sometimes represented by Bt, where B is equated through $(d\varepsilon/dt)$ to (σ/η). However, although η is an inconsistent quantity in rock, it has a sufficiently high value at low temperatures (10^{10}–10^{20} kg/m-sec) to render B insignificant compared with the other terms. In fact secondary creep only exists at temperatures of between $0.2T$ and $0.5T$, where T is the absolute melting temperature of rock; and cannot therefore exist below a temperature of 300–$400\,°K$ (say $100\,°C$).

It can readily be seen that eqn (4.13) is analogous to primary flow of a Kelvin or Zener body, with the rate of strain,

$$\frac{d\varepsilon}{dt} = At^{-1} \qquad (4.14)$$

reducing to zero at infinite time. The applicability of eqn (4.13) to rocks has been confirmed by various workers (Murrell and Misra, 1962; Robertson, 1964; Parsons and Hedley, 1966). Typical strain/time curves for various rock types at different stress levels are shown in Figure 4.4.

Equations (4.13) and (4.14) give the relationship between time and strain at constant stress. Obviously since they reflect only two of the three variables affecting time-dependent deformation, they must be expanded to include the third, namely stress.

Various attempts have been made to suggest a form relating stress and strain rate, the most commonly quoted being an empirical relationship in the form:

$$\frac{d\varepsilon}{dt} = C(\sigma_1 - \sigma_3)^n \qquad (4.15)$$

This is obviously unsatisfactory from the point of view of any type of analysis, since C can never be constant, but it may be expanded on the basis of available results in the approximate form:

$$\frac{d\varepsilon}{dt} = \frac{1}{t}\left(\frac{\sigma_1 - \sigma_3}{2G}\right)^n \qquad (4.16)$$

where n is a constant exponent equal to between 1 and 2 at low stresses and rising to between 2 and 3 for high stresses (Robertson, 1964), G is the modulus of rigidity and $(\sigma_1 - \sigma_3)/2$ represents the maximum shear stress.

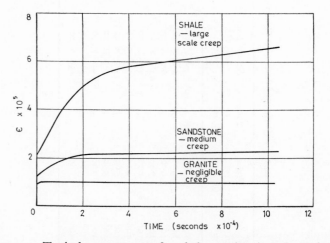

Figure 4.4 Typical creep curves for shale, sandstone and granite at 100 kg/cm² constant stress and room temperature.

In the case of uniaxial stress, the instantaneous normal stress, σ, can be substituted for the shear stress and the modulus of elasticity E for G.

By integration an expression for the instantaneous creep strain can be obtained as:

$$\varepsilon = \left(\frac{\sigma_1 - \sigma_3}{2G}\right)^n \log_e t \qquad (4.17)$$

TABLE 4.1 Effect of Stress on Creep Constants

Rock	Modulus of Elasticity E (kg/cm^2)	Stress σ (kg/cm^2)	Time t (sec)	Strain Rate $d\epsilon/dt$ sec^{-1}	$\dfrac{\sigma}{E}$	A	n
Granite	$7 \cdot 38 \times 10^5$	1,380	$1 \cdot 38 \times 10^4$	$4 \cdot 0 \times 10^{-10}$	$1 \cdot 87 \times 10^{-3}$	$5 \cdot 5 \times 10^{-6}$	$1 \cdot 91$
Peridotite	$5 \cdot 52 \times 10^5$	980	,,	$2 \cdot 4 \times 10^{-10}$	$1 \cdot 77 \times 10^{-3}$	$3 \cdot 2 \times 10^{-6}$	$1 \cdot 99$
Haematite	$7 \cdot 45 \times 10^5$	970	,,	$6 \cdot 2 \times 10^{-10}$	$1 \cdot 30 \times 10^{-3}$	$8 \cdot 6 \times 10^{-6}$	$1 \cdot 75$
Limestone	$5 \cdot 89 \times 10^5$	1,390	,,	$11 \cdot 3 \times 10^{-10}$	$2 \cdot 36 \times 10^{-3}$	$15 \cdot 6 \times 10^{-6}$	$1 \cdot 83$
Limestone	$7 \cdot 10 \times 10^5$	670	,,	$4 \cdot 2 \times 10^{-10}$	$0 \cdot 95 \times 10^{-3}$	$5 \cdot 8 \times 10^{-6}$	$1 \cdot 40$
Sandstone	$1 \cdot 0 \times 10^5$	420	,,	$3 \cdot 6 \times 10^{-10}$	$4 \cdot 20 \times 10^{-3}$	$5 \cdot 0 \times 10^{-6}$	$1 \cdot 81$
Chlorite	$6 \cdot 09 \times 10^5$	560	,,	$4 \cdot 0 \times 10^{-10}$	$0 \cdot 92 \times 10^{-3}$	$5 \cdot 5 \times 10^{-6}$	$1 \cdot 37$
Blastonite	$4 \cdot 53 \times 10^5$	590	,,	$3 \cdot 8 \times 10^{-10}$	$1 \cdot 20 \times 10^{-3}$	$5 \cdot 2 \times 10^{-6}$	$1 \cdot 95$
Shale	$1 \cdot 30 \times 10^5$	300	,,	$29 \cdot 4 \times 10^{-10}$	$2 \cdot 30 \times 10^{-3}$	40×10^{-6}	$1 \cdot 67$
Potash	$0 \cdot 73 \times 10^5$	60	,,	167×10^{-10}	$0 \cdot 82 \times 10^{-3}$	230×10^{-6}	$1 \cdot 20$
Rock Salt	$1 \cdot 84 \times 10^5$	80	,,	236×10^{-10}	$0 \cdot 43 \times 10^{-3}$	320×10^{-6}	$1 \cdot 03$

in the direction of maximum shear stress under triaxial stress conditions and

$$\varepsilon = \left(\frac{\sigma}{E}\right)^n \log_e t \tag{4.18}$$

under uniaxial stress conditions.

Thus by equating eqn (4.13) to eqns (4.17) and (4.18), an expression for the creep constant A can be obtained in the form:

$$A = \left(\frac{\sigma}{E}\right)^n = \left(\frac{\sigma_1 - \sigma_3}{2G}\right)^n \tag{4.19}$$

where $E \simeq 2G$ (cf. Chapter 3).

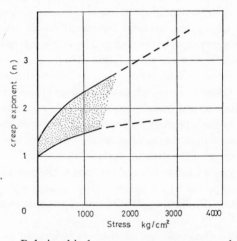

Figure 4.5   Relationship between creep exponent and stress.

There should therefore be a range of values of A for all rocks, related in some way to the measured modulus of elasticity and the applied stress, through a constant exponent, n, where n is dependent primarily on the stress magnitude.

This is demonstrated in Table 4.1, based on the results of Coates and Parsons (1966) and Parsons and Hedley (1966) for a diverse selection of rocks subject to varying uniaxial stresses. Whilst obviously incomplete, there is certainly evidence to support a tentative conclusion that n will be somewhat greater than unity at low stresses, rising to $n = 2$ at stresses in the region of 1,500 kg/cm². Figure 4.5 shows this, and also includes results collected by Robertson (1964).

4.3 Flow Properties of Rocks

So far creep has been considered primarily as a qualitative phenomenon. Unless, however, creep can be defined quantitatively for a
specific rock, it is of marginal use as a design parameter. As already
stated, the coefficient of linear viscosity varies so much as to be virtually useless in defining the flow properties of a rock. It is in any case
confusing since it suggests that the mechanism of flow or creep in rock is
similar to that of flow in fluids. This is, of course, far from the truth;
there are various explanations for flow in rocks, but it is only suggested
that anything approaching viscous flow occurs under full tectonic stress
and temperature conditions or possibly under dynamic load conditions.
Under normal stress conditions at low temperatures, the primary creep
mechanism (stage b) appears to be dominated initially by slip along pre-
existing weakness planes in the rock and by brittle fracture and cracking
inside the rock (Robertson, 1960), followed in the secondary creep stage,
if the temperature is sufficiently high, by less significant plastic flow
mechanisms (Heard, 1963) such as twinning and translation gliding and
by recrystallization and dislocation. These latter may be of considerable
significance in both primary and secondary stages in rocks which are
known to have a high degree of plasticity – but they are, by and large,
beyond the scope of the present work.

The theory of microfracture and cracking as the major creep mechanism can be supported by the susceptibility of rocks and other materials
to *fatigue* failure (Phillips, 1948) following repeated loading at low stress
levels.

If, therefore, the coefficient of viscosity is ignored as a quantitative
time-strain parameter, there remain two interrelated empirically based
constants, the stress-dependent *creep constant A* and the slightly un-
reliable *creep exponent n*, also stress-dependent but over a smaller
range.

Values of A calculated from Robertson's compilation are quoted in
Table 4.2. Taken together with those in Table 4.1, it is evident that
although values of A vary considerably with stress (particularly at high
stresses), there seems to be confirmation of the relationship noticeable
at similar stresses between A and the strength/elasticity parameters of
rock. Values of A at 100 kg/cm^2 stress appear to range from the order of
10^{-6} for harder igneous rocks, up to 10^{-3} for weaker sedimentary rocks.
One important factor, however, is that the duration of the test does not
appear to affect the value of A significantly; thus although there may

not yet be sufficient information available to classify A as a specific design parameter, there is no reason why a value of A obtained from a relatively simple creep test under specified stress conditions, should not be extrapolated for the full creep range. This means that whilst it is impossible to quote a value of A for a particular type of rock with confidence, it is possible to define the significance of an experimentally obtained value of A in the design of a structure in rock.

For instance, suppose a rock with a modulus of elasticity equal to 10^6 kg/cm² is compressively loaded at a stress level of 100 kg/cm², giving

TABLE 4.2   Creep Data for Rocks (Room Temperature)
(Compiled by Robertson, 1964)

Rock	t (sec)	$\sigma_1 - \sigma_3$ (kg/cm²)	ϵ	A
Granite	$1 \cdot 7 \times 10^5$	1,000	10^{-4}	$8 \cdot 5 \times 10^{-6}$
	$1 \cdot 0 \times 10^6$	1,000	10^{-4}	$7 \cdot 2 \times 10^{-6}$
	$8 \cdot 6 \times 10^2$	1,000	10^{-3}	$1 \cdot 7 \times 10^{-4}$
Granodiorite	$2 \cdot 6 \times 10^5$	100	10^{-4}	$8 \cdot 2 \times 10^{-6}$
	$5 \cdot 2 \times 10^5$	100	10^{-5}	$7 \cdot 8 \times 10^{-7}$
Rhyolite	$8 \cdot 6 \times 10^7$	100	10^{-4}	$5 \cdot 5 \times 10^{-6}$
Andesite	$1 \cdot 2 \times 10^6$	100	10^{-5}	$7 \cdot 1 \times 10^{-7}$
Grabbro	$2 \cdot 6 \times 10^5$	100	10^{-5}	$8 \cdot 3 \times 10^{-7}$
Basalt	$5 \cdot 2 \times 10^5$	100	10^{-4}	$8 \cdot 0 \times 10^{-6}$
Quartzite	$1 \cdot 7 \times 10^6$	100	10^{-3}	$7 \cdot 0 \times 10^{-5}$
Sandstone	$8 \cdot 6 \times 10^2$	1	10^{-2}	$1 \cdot 7 \times 10^{-3}$
Shale	$8 \cdot 6 \times 10^4$	100	10^{-3}	$9 \cdot 1 \times 10^{-5}$
	$1 \cdot 2 \times 10^8$	10	10^{-2}	$5 \cdot 4 \times 10^{-4}$
Limestone	$8 \cdot 6 \times 10^4$	1,000	7×10^{-3}	$6 \cdot 4 \times 10^{-3}$
Rock Salt	$3 \cdot 1 \times 10^6$	100	10^{-2}	$2 \cdot 1 \times 10^{-4}$
	$8 \cdot 6 \times 10^4$	100	2×10^{-3}	$3 \cdot 0 \times 10^{-3}$

an elastic strain of 10^{-4}. If the rock has a creep constant equal to 10^{-6}, then the total creep strain over a period of (say) ten years will be approximately equal to 2×10^{-5}, or nearly an order of magnitude less than the elastic strain; in other words it is not significant. On the other hand if A were equal to 10^{-4}, then over the same period the creep strain would be approximately 2×10^{-3}, an order of magnitude greater than the elastic strain and of critical significance.

A full range of creep/strain constant and elastic strain/modulus of elasticity values is plotted in Figure 4.6. This shows that for the average design parameters chosen ($\sigma = 100$ kg/cm², $t = 10$ years) a rock with a modulus of elasticity above 5×10^5 kg/cm² will for the purpose of design be wholly elastic if A is of the order of magnitude of 10^{-6} or less and wholly anelastic (i.e. viscous) if A is of the order of magnitude of 10^{-4} or greater. For values of A between these values both elastic and time-dependent flow properties of the rock must be considered. This type of construction may be used for any stress/duration values required.

Where creep-testing facilities are not available, A may be obtained approximately at any stress or maximum stress difference for a rock whose elastic modulus (or strength) is known, by assuming a value for

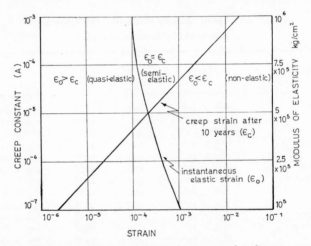

Figure 4.6   Relative values of elastic and creep strain after ten years for different values of E and A. σ is constant at 100 kg/cm^2.

the creep exponent, n, in eqn (4.19). Some suggested values for n and their equivalent A value are quoted in Table 4.3. They may be compared with actual values in Table 4.2.

On this basis the elastic category of rock will include most of the rocks with E values greater than 5 or 6 $\times$ 10^5 kg/cm^2, depending on the stress magnitude already described in Chapter 3 as quasi-elastic (primarily igneous rocks). Most sedimentary rocks – even fine-grained limestones and sandstones – must be included in the second semi-elastic category even though their modulus of elasticity may exceed 5 $\times$ 10^5 kg/cm^2, because of their tendency to flow under high stresses. At low stress levels, however, these rocks can be considered wholly elastic within limits prescribed by the presence or absence of discontinuities.

The third category includes shales and the weaker sedimentary rocks, where creep can become a serious problem even at low stresses and in which structures must be initially designed to withstand high deformation due to post-construction creep.

These three creep categories readily substantiate the 'elastic' categories of Section 3.2. This forms the basis of a simple rock property classification (Chapter 13) with three distinct rock types designated quasi-elastic, semi-elastic and non-elastic.

4.4 Creep as a Design Factor in Rock

If the reactions of a rock are wholly elastic, its structural properties may be analysed solely in terms of stress leading to brittle failure – the convention with most quasi-elastic engineering materials. However, as

TABLE 4.3   Calculated Values of A for Various Stress Conditions

Type of Rock	E $(kg/cm^2$ $\times 10^{-5})$	$\sigma = 100 \ kg/cm^2$ $n = 1.5$	$\sigma = 500 \ kg/cm^2$ $n = 1.7$	$\sigma = 1,000 \ kg/cm^2$ $n = 1.85$
Quasi-elastic	12	7.6×10^{-7}	1.8×10^{-6}	2.2×10^{-6}
	10	1.0×10^{-6}	2.4×10^{-6}	2.9×10^{-6}
	8	1.4×10^{-6}	3.5×10^{-6}	4.3×10^{-6}
Semi-elastic	6	2.1×10^{-6}	5.8×10^{-6}	7.4×10^{-6}
	4	4.0×10^{-6}	1.2×10^{-5}	1.5×10^{-5}
Non-elastic	2	1.1×10^{-5}	3.8×10^{-5}	5.3×10^{-5}
	0.5	8.9×10^{-5}	1.6×10^{-4}	2.5×10^{-3}

time-strain increases in a rock, so the initial peak stress level becomes less important and the physical fact of deformation more important, so that eventually it may be desirable to express rock properties in terms of deformation characteristics associated with a specific stress level rather than in terms of the apparent stress/strain relationship.

This requires a radical readjustment of design processes, since the instantaneous stress failure level or *strength* on which they are normally based becomes an arbitrary parameter which will have little or no significance over a prolonged period of time – when a structure in rock while resisting brittle failure may be destroyed by sub-failure deformation. It is therefore imperative in a rock with *substantial* time-dependent characteristics that some form of reinforcement – however undesirable – be introduced, the amount and magnitude depending on the life of the structure. Alternatively, stress levels may be reduced sufficiently to eliminate serious time-strain effects.

The latter approach, which is extended in Chapter 11, will be the better solution in semi- and quasi-elastic rocks, the former in non-elastic rocks.

5

Strength and Failure in Rocks

The strength of a material in a mechanical sense may be defined as the ability of the material to resist stress without large-scale failure. Since large-scale failure in quasi-elastic materials only occurs beyond the elastic stress limit, this is the most commonly quoted strength parameter for rock – particularly so in those rocks which may be considered brittle materials and in which the elastic limit immediately precedes failure. In non-elastic rocks whose reactions are complicated by considerable anelastic deformation, the strength, particularly in confinement, may be difficult to define satisfactorily and may be of minor significance in practice.

The present chapter describes several criteria which may be used to define failure in a rock. The term criterion is advisedly used since in a material where so little is known of mechanisms of deformation and failure, it is impossible to devise a theory which will fit all rocks, in all states. For instance, in Chapter 1 it was suggested that the strength of individual minerals might determine the strength property of a rock, and yet it is not abnormal to find limestones and dolomites which are stronger than some siliceous igneous rocks. Probably the only strength parameter capable of simple definition is uniaxial strength, which can be used as a basis for strength criteria but has little practical use in isolation.

5.1 Uniaxial Strength

Uniaxial strength defines the failure of a finite rock specimen subject to stress in one direction. Its value is affected by two primary factors: the type of stress leading to failure (compressive, tensile or shear) and the type of test used to determine strength. The type of stress is particularly important in the case of rock, whose brittle characteristics are typified by an apparently high compressive strength and relatively low shear and tensile strengths. The type of testing and its effect on strength magnitude is of less importance provided the soundness of the test is proved (Chapter 7) and its implications understood.

Strength values are defined according to the type of test; thus *compressive* strength (sometimes crushing strength) is normally defined as the stress required to crush a cylindrical rock sample unconfined at its sides. *True* compressive failure in a rock can only occur through internal collapse of the rock structure due to compression of pore space resulting in grain fracture and movement along grain and crystal boundaries. The true compressive strength of a rock is therefore influenced by its internal structure, and sedimentary rocks with a relatively large amount of pore space will tend to be weaker in compression than fine-grained metamorphic or igneous rocks.

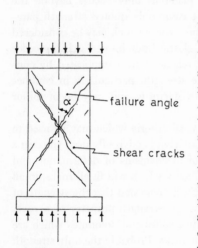

Figure 5.1 Shear failure in compression.

Since true compressive failure would require hydrostatic loading conditions, and would in any case be difficult to detect, the compressive strength of a rock specimen is, in many ways, a reflection of its *shear* strength. This is the stress at which an unconfined rock fails in shear, and since a cylinder of rock in a crushing test would be expected to fail primarily in shear (Figure 5.1), the compressive strength might be more accurately described as the shear failure level under the conditions of the compressive strength test. For instance, in a cylindrical specimen under compressive stress, the compressive strength (S_c) will increase as the length/diameter ratio decreases (Obert *et al.*, 1946) in the form:

$$S_c = S_{c_0}\left(0.8 + \frac{0.2}{L/D}\right) \qquad (5.1)$$

where S_{c_0} is the compressive strength accepted as standard where $L/D = 1$.

This means that as L/D rises there is a tendency towards a constant compressive strength, related in some way to the unconfined shear strength, although not necessarily equal to it, and as L/D approaches zero the compressive strength will become infinitely large in conditions similar to hydrostatic loading.

There is therefore no true compressive strength and hence no failure in compression when rocks are loaded. Hence all criteria of failure in rocks are based on failure in shear or in tension.

Since most problems in rock design involve compressive stresses, the concept of *tensile* strength in rocks can normally only be used indirectly. It is, however, of paramount importance in the Griffith criterion of failure and in the dynamic fracturing of rocks by explosive action. It is a property of brittle materials that their tensile strength is considerably

TABLE 5.1   Uniaxial Compressive and Tensile Strengths

Rock	S_c (kg/cm^2)	S_T (kg/cm^2)
Granite	1,000–2,500	70–250
Diorite	1,800–3,000	150–300
Dolerite	2,000–3,500	150–350
Gabbro	1,800–3,000	150–300
Basalt	1,500–3,000	100–300
Sandstone	200–1,700	40–250
Shale	100–1,000	20–100
Limestone	300–2,500	50–250
Dolomite	800–2,500	150–250
Coal	50– 500	20–50
Quartzite	1,500–3,000	100–300
Gneiss	500–2,000	50–200
Marble	1,000–2,500	70–200
Slate	1,000–2,000	70–200

less than their apparent compressive strength. This is the case in all rocks and in the case of the more brittle rocks; there appears to be a general linear relationship between tensile (S_T) and compressive strength (S_c) (Hosking, 1955), taking an approximate form:

$$S_c = KS_T \qquad (5.2)$$

where K varies between 4 and 10 depending on the type of rock.

Thus (see Chapter 3) tensile strength can be related through compressive strength to the modulus of elasticity. The relationship between shear strength and compressive strength is discussed in the following section. Typical compressive and tensile strength values are listed in Table 5.1.

5.2 Strength of Rocks in Confinement

Uniaxial strength, as discussed in Section 5.1, is an arbitrary rock property depending primarily on the conditions of the test used in its determination. Under these conditions failure is easily defined and often evident in the violent reaction of the specimen under test at the moment of failure. Even so, the actual point of failure can be affected by the shape and dimensions of the specimen, the rate of loading and many other factors. It is evident, therefore, that the failure of rock in mass, subject to various and often varying confining stress conditions, will be extremely complicated.

The triaxial conditions of loading found in a rock in mass will consist of the three principal stresses σ_1, σ_2, σ_3, acting mutually at right angles. Numerous criteria have been devised to explain the conditions for failure of a material under such a system of loading, and of these, three have been applied with varying degrees of success in rocks, to predict the relationship between the principal stresses at failure and the strength of a rock. These are the *Coulomb* criterion of failure at maximum shear stress, the *Mohr* criterion of shear failure and the *Griffith* criterion of tensile failure.

The simplest of these is that based on the *maximum shear stress* criterion of Coulomb. This states that failure occurs at a point in a material where the maximum shear stress (τ_M), equal to half the difference between the major and minor principal stresses (Chapter 2), is equivalent to the shear strength (S_s) of the material and that failure occurs on a plane bisecting the angle between the two extreme principal stresses, i.e.

$$\tau_M = \tfrac{1}{2}(\sigma_1 - \sigma_3) = S_s \tag{5.3}$$

This criterion can be extended in the form of the *Coulomb–Navier* criterion of failure which assumes that on the plane of shear failure on which the shear stress acts and on which a normal stress (σ) also acts, the shear strength is reinforced by an amount $\mu\sigma$ (Figure 5.2), which is analogous to the tangential friction force acting between a sliding body and an inclined plane. Since the frictional resistance is equal to the product of the normal force and the coefficient of friction, the imaginary constant μ is known as the *coefficient of internal friction*, and eqn (5.3) becomes

$$\tau = S_s + \mu\sigma \tag{5.4}$$

If the stresses acting in the plane of maximum and minimum principal stress are considered, eqn (5.4) may be expanded in terms of eqns (2.9) and (2.10) to give

$$S_s = \tau - \mu\sigma$$

$$= \frac{(\sigma_1 - \sigma_3)}{2}\sin 2\alpha - \frac{(\sigma_1 + \sigma_3)}{2}\mu - \frac{(\sigma_1 - \sigma_3)}{2}\mu\cos 2\alpha \quad (5.5)$$

$$= -\mu\frac{(\sigma_1 + \sigma_3)}{2} + \frac{(\sigma_1 - \sigma_3)}{2}(\sin 2\alpha - \mu\cos 2\alpha) \quad (5.6)$$

where α, substituted for θ, becomes the *angle of shear failure* (Figure 5.1).

It can be seen from this analysis that S_s will have a maximum value where $\tan 2\alpha = -1/\mu$, this being equal to:

$$S_s(\text{MAX}) = -\mu\frac{(\sigma_1 + \sigma_3)}{2} + \frac{(\sigma_1 - \sigma_3)}{2}(1 + \mu^2)^{\frac{1}{2}} \quad (5.7)$$

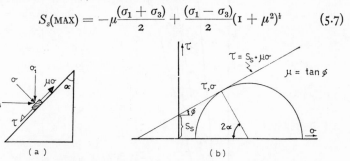

(a) (b)

Figure 5.2 Coulomb–Navier criterion of failure.

Thus failure will occur when:

$$2S_s \leqslant \sigma_1[-\mu + (\mu^2 + 1)^{\frac{1}{2}}] - \sigma_3[\mu + (\mu^2 + 1)^{\frac{1}{2}}] \quad (5.8)$$

which leads to a criterion for failure under uniaxial stress in either tension or compression.

For instance, for failure in tension $\sigma_1 = 0$, $\sigma_3 = -S_T$ (tensile strength) and for failure in compression $\sigma_1 = S_c$ (compressive strength), $\sigma_3 = 0$.

Thus

$$2S_s = S_T[\mu + (\mu^2 + 1)^{\frac{1}{2}}] \quad (5.9)$$

$$2S_s = S_c[-\mu + (\mu^2 + 1)^{\frac{1}{2}}] \quad (5.10)$$

and

$$\frac{S_T}{S_c} = \frac{-\mu + (\mu^2 + 1)^{\frac{1}{2}}}{\mu + (\mu^2 + 1)^{\frac{1}{2}}} \quad (5.11)$$

This illustrates the fact that compressive strength would normally be greater than tensile strength.

Thus by substituting eqns (5.9) and (5.10) in eqn (5.8):

$$\frac{\sigma_1}{S_c} - \frac{\sigma_3}{S_T} = 1 \quad (5.12)$$

and therefore
$$\sigma_1 = S_c + \frac{S_c}{S_T}\sigma_3 \qquad (5.13)$$

The extent of the compromise between this idealized solution and the actuality found in laboratory stress measurements can be illustrated by plotting the results of a series of triaxial test observations collected by Hoek (1966) from a variety of sources on axes representing σ_1/S_c and σ_3/S_c (Figure 5.3). The rocks are represented in three main groups –

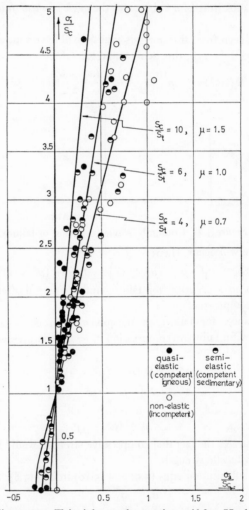

Figure 5.3 Triaxial test observations. (After Hoek.)

competent igneous rocks, competent sedimentary rocks and incompetent sedimentary rocks, and σ_1 and σ_3 represent the major and minor principal stresses at the actual point of failure.

The results fall into three general failure patterns: for competent igneous rocks:

$$\frac{\sigma_1}{S_c} = 10\left(\frac{\sigma_3}{S_T}\right) + 1 \tag{5.14}$$

for competent sedimentary rocks:

$$\frac{\sigma_1}{S_c} = 6\left(\frac{\sigma_3}{S_T}\right) + 1 \tag{5.15}$$

and for incompetent sedimentary rocks:

$$\frac{\sigma_1}{S_c} = 4\left(\frac{\sigma_3}{S_T}\right) + 1 \tag{5.16}$$

Compressive stresses only are considered.

This confirms the form of eqns (5.12) and (5.13) and also the general form of linearity previously encountered between compressive and tensile strengths. It must be noted, however, that, particularly at low values and negative values of stress, there is a distinct tendency for non-linearity in the Coulomb–Navier criterion, suggesting that for an exact criterion of failure in rock an alternative form must be sought.

As a general rule, however, the ratio S_c/S_T may be taken as 10 in competent igneous rocks (cf. quasi-elastic), 6 in competent sedimentary rocks (semi-elastic) and 4 in incompetent sedimentary rocks (non-elastic).

From eqns (5.9) and (5.10) this ratio may be used to obtain a value for the coefficient of internal friction thus:

$$\frac{S_c}{S_T} = \frac{(\mu^2 + 1)^{\frac{1}{2}} + \mu}{(\mu^2 + 1)^{\frac{1}{2}} - \mu} \tag{5.17}$$

giving approximate values of $\mu = 1\cdot5$ where $S_c/S_T = 10$, $\mu = 1\cdot0$ where $S_c/S_T = 6$ and $\mu = 0\cdot7$ where $S_c/S_T = 4$. If these values are substituted in eqn (5.10), theoretical equations for S_s can be obtained approximately in the form:

$$\begin{aligned}
S_s &= 0\cdot15 S_c = 1\cdot5 S_T \quad \text{(quasi-elastic)} \\
S_s &= 0\cdot02 S_c = 1\cdot2 S_T \quad \text{(semi-elastic)} \\
S_s &= 0\cdot025 S_c = S_T \quad \text{(non-elastic)}
\end{aligned} \right\} \tag{5.18}$$

where S_s is the *uniaxial shear strength*.

These values may be compared with actual measurements quoted in

Table 5.2 (U.S. Bureau of Reclamation, 1953; Schwartz, 1964; and others) which are in fact slightly larger – suggesting an empirical relationship of the form $S_s = 2S_T$ for competent rocks and $S_s = 1/2S_c$ for less competent rocks.

TABLE 5.2   Shear Strength and Angles and Coefficients of Internal Friction

Rock	S_s (kg/cm²)	ϕ	μ
Granite	140–500	45°–60°	1·0–1·8
Dolerite	250–600	55°–60°	1·4–1·8
Basalt	200–600	50°–55°	1·2–1·4
Sandstone	80–400	35°–50°	0·7–1·2
Shale	30–300	15°–30°	0·25–0·6
Limestone	100–500	35°–50°	0·7–1·2
Quartzite	200–600	50°–60°	1·2–1·8
Marble	150–300	35°–50°	0·7–1·2

With this empirical data it is now possible to obtain a Coulomb–Navier failure envelope under triaxial stress conditions for different rock types. As stated theoretically, the Coulomb–Navier failure envelope (eqn 5.4) appears as a straight line with slope μ on a plot of τ vs. σ (Figure 5.2). If data for S_s, S_T and μ are included, however, for each of the three cases considered, a slightly altered picture takes shape (Figure 5.4), giving a curved envelope in the tensile zone and a straight

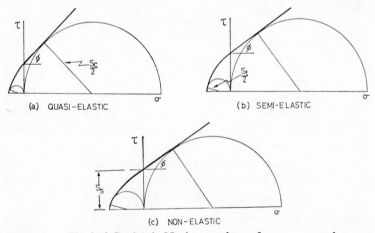

(a) QUASI–ELASTIC   (b) SEMI–ELASTIC

(c) NON–ELASTIC

Figure 5.4   Typical Coulomb–Navier envelopes for average rock types.

line of slope tan ϕ in the compressive zone. This envelope can be constructed for any rock, providing the uniaxial compressive and uniaxial tensile strengths are known for the rock, and can be used in conjunction with the Mohr circle construction (Section 2.2) to estimate the magnitude of stress difference to cause shear failure at any point in the rock.

Although used extensively to predict failure in rocks, the Coulomb–Navier criterion does not represent exactly the failure envelope of most rocks (Figure 5.5) which tend to have a major curvilinear zone even in

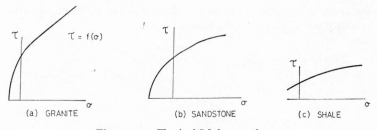

Figure 5.5   Typical Mohr envelopes.

compression. In accurate work it is therefore sometimes preferable to treat the effects of failure in shear in a more empirical form under the general heading of *Mohr's criterion of failure*.

5.3 Mohr Criterion of Failure

It has been shown that all triaxial stress systems may be represented by three principal stresses which by definition act orthogonally and that each pair of principal stresses may be further resolved into a normal and shear stress acting on a plane. Each of these planes may be represented by a Mohr stress circle (Section 2.2) and from these it can be seen that maximum shear stress occurs in the plane containing the major and minor principal stresses. Thus when a rock is confined triaxially, failure will occur when the shear stress in the plane of major and minor principal stress exceeds the shear strength of the rock.

This restatement of the Coulomb–Navier criterion forms the basis of the Mohr criterion of failure as applied to rocks and soils, which states that at failure, the normal and shear stresses in the plane of failure will be related in the form:

$$\tau = f(\sigma) \qquad (5.19)$$

This forms the general equation of the *Mohr envelope*, relating shear strength to normal stress, which marks the boundary between failure and resistance in a rock subject to triaxial stress. The stress circles (Figure 2.5) of radius $(\sigma_1 - \sigma_3)/2$ and centre $(\sigma_1 + \sigma_3)/2$, o, which come into contact with the envelope, represent the principal stress conditions under which the maximum shear stress in the plane equals the shear strength of the rock – in other words the condition for failure. The point where the envelope meets the ordinate represents the shear strength at zero confining pressure, and the anticlockwise angle 2α between the abscissa and the radius normal to the curve represents twice the angle α between the plane of failure and the direction of major principal stress, known as the *angle of failure*.

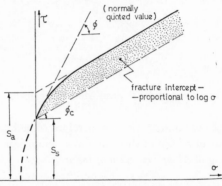

Figure 5.6   General form of Mohr envelope.

The simplest form of Mohr envelope is a straight line representing the original Coulomb–Navier criterion of failure, with slope equal to the coefficient of internal friction or $\tan \phi$ where ϕ is the *angle of internal friction*. Since by symmetry $\phi = 90° - 2\alpha$, then $\tan \phi = (1 - \tan \alpha)/(1 + \tan \alpha)$. The normal form of Mohr envelope for a rock, built up from a series of triaxial tests, can be generalized in the form shown in Figure 5.6. In this case, following the shear intercept there is a zone of decreasing slope, eventually forming a near-constant slope straight line at higher stress values which may be extrapolated back to give an apparent shear intercept S_a. If an angle of internal friction is quoted for a rock, the value normally given is an average value of slope near the ordinate intercept rather than the constant value or the tangent at the ordinate intercept. Schwartz (1964) suggests an equation for the rock envelope in the general form:

$$\tau = S_s + \sigma \tan \phi_c + I_p \qquad (5.20)$$

where ϕ_c is the minimum constant value of the angle of internal friction, and I_p is a factor known as the fracture interference function, proportional to log σ (Figure 5.6).

This is a purely empirical approach to the Mohr envelope. A theoretical solution to the curved envelope can be obtained through the Griffith theory of failure, which considers the tensile strength of the rock.

5.4 Griffith Criterion of Brittle Failure

The Griffith theories of fracture (Griffith, 1924) originally devised for glass, and adapted by Orowan (1951), Brace (1960) and Hoek (1965) for rock, postulate that fracture is initiated in a brittle material by tensile failure around the tops of micro-cracks and flaws present in the material. The first theory dealing with the actual mechanisms of crack propagation in a uniaxial stress field has limited application. The second theory which explains the condition for propagation of a crack in a biaxial stress field has wide applications in rock engineering. The basic assumption in the solution for a crack in a stress field (as in the Mohr theory the plane of major/minor principal stress is considered) is that the crack is elliptical and flat (Figure 5.7).

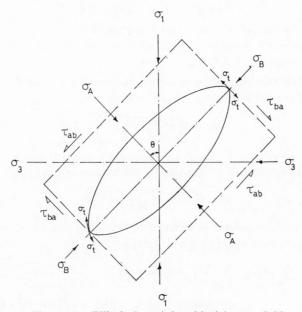

Figure 5.7 Elliptical crack in a biaxial stress field.

An extension of the theory to three dimensions (Sack, 1946) postulates a circular crack in the intermediate principal plane. It can be shown, however, that neither the intermediate principal stress nor the shape of the crack in that plane has any practical significance.

In the biaxial case, the stress system acting on the crack can be resolved into a normal and shear component σ_A and τ_{AB}, since it can be assumed that the stress acting axially along the crack σ_B will have negligible influence on the stress at its tip. A, B, are the axes of the crack. σ_A and τ_{AB} can be related to σ_1 and σ_3 as in eqns (2.9) and (2.10).

$$\sigma_A = \frac{\sigma_1 + \sigma_3}{2} - \frac{\sigma_1 - \sigma_3}{2} \cos 2\theta \qquad (5.21)$$

$$\tau_{AB} = \frac{\sigma_1 - \sigma_3}{2} \sin 2\theta \qquad (5.22)$$

σ_A and τ_{AB} will induce a tangential stress on the crack boundary given by (Inglis):

$$\sigma_T = \frac{\sigma_A(\sinh 2R_0 + \exp(2R_0)\cos 2T - 1) + 2\tau_{AB}\exp(2R_0)\sin 2T}{\cosh 2R_0 - \cos 2T} \qquad (5.23)$$

where R, T are the elliptical co-ordinates where:

$$x = c \sinh R \sin T, \ z = c \cosh R \cos T$$

R_0 is the value of R on the crack boundary, and
c represents a complex constant which can be equated to half the crack length when $R = R_0$.

Since the maximum value of σ_T will occur at the ends of the crack where T is small this (eqn 5.23) can be restated:

$$\sigma_T = 2\left(\frac{\sigma_A R_0 + \tau_{AB}T}{R_0^2 + T^2}\right) \qquad (5.24)$$

The co-ordinate T where $\sigma_T = \sigma_T(\text{MAX})$, $\sigma_T(\text{MIN})$ can then be obtained from $\partial \sigma_T / \partial T = 0$, giving by substitution in eqn (5.24):

$$\sigma_T = \frac{\sigma_A \pm \sqrt{(\sigma_A{}^2 + \tau_{AB}{}^2)}}{R_0} \qquad (5.25)$$

which can be expressed in terms of the principal stresses σ_1, σ_3, by substitution from eqns (5.21) and (5.22) as:

$$\sigma_T = \frac{1}{2R_0}[(\sigma_1 + \sigma_3) - (\sigma_1 - \sigma_3)\cos 2\theta]$$

$$\pm \frac{1}{4R_0{}^2}[(\sigma_1{}^2 + \sigma_3{}^2) - (\sigma_1{}^2 - \sigma_3{}^2)\cos 2\theta]^{\frac{1}{2}} \qquad (5.26)$$

The angle of the crack at which maximal stresses are induced at its tip is given from $d\sigma_T(\text{MAX})/d\theta = 0$, whence

$$\cos 2\alpha = \frac{\sigma_1 - \sigma_3}{2(\sigma_1 + \sigma_3)} \qquad (5.27)$$

Equations (5.26) and (5.27) give the theoretical conditions for crack failure in terms, therefore, of six major parameters $\sigma_T(\text{MAX})$, σ_1, σ_3, R_0 (which defines the crack shape), θ and α, which may be termed the critical crack orientation. Thus by substituting α for θ in eqn. (5.26) the conditions for failure can be written as:

$$\sigma_T(\text{MAX})R_0 = 2\sigma_3 \geqslant 2S_T \qquad (5.28)$$

where S_T is the tensile strength of the rock.

In other words the rock will fail when $S_T = \sigma_3$. Since $\sigma_T(\text{MAX})$ and R_0 are imaginary quantities, the device of substituting $2S_T = \sigma_T(\text{MAX})R_0$ in eqn (5.26) allows the problem to be treated quantitatively, thus failure will occur when:

$$S_T = \tfrac{1}{2}[(\sigma_1 + \sigma_3) - (\sigma_1 - \sigma_3)\cos 2\alpha]$$
$$\pm \tfrac{1}{4}[(\sigma_1{}^2 + \sigma_3{}^2) - (\sigma_1{}^2 - \sigma_3{}^2)\cos 2\alpha] \qquad (5.29)$$

This would apply to an anisotropic bedded rock, where the orientation of the cracks would be assumed parallel or normal to the bedding planes. In a homogeneous, isotropic material, it is assumed that cracks have random orientation and would fail initially in the direction represented by α, resulting in the fracture criterion:

$$S_T = \frac{-(\sigma_1 - \sigma_3)^2}{8(\sigma_1 + \sigma_3)} \qquad (5.30)$$

It is interesting to note that when $\sigma_3 = 0$, the uniaxial compressive strength represented by σ_1 is equal to $8S_T$. This is quite near the experimental relationship obtained from the Coulomb–Navier criterion, and suggests that the Griffith theory may reflect reasonably accurately the condition for failure in *competent* rock.

The quadratic relationship expressed in eqn (5.30) can be readily expressed as the equation of a Mohr envelope (Murrell, 1963). The system of Mohr stress circles under this envelope may be expressed in the general form:

$$\left(\sigma - \frac{\sigma_1 + \sigma_3}{2}\right)^2 + \tau^2 = \left(\frac{\sigma_1 - \sigma_3}{2}\right)^2 \qquad (5.31)$$

and by substitution and partial differentiation in terms of $(\sigma_1 + \sigma_3)/2$ the equation of the envelope becomes:

$$\tau^2 - 4S_T\sigma = 4S_T{}^2 \qquad (5.32)$$

a parabolic equation yielding a curve similar to the Mohr envelope in Figure 5.6, with an intercept equivalent to $S_s = 2S_T$ (Figure 5.8). This is also close to that found in practice.

In deriving the Griffith criterion for failure, it is assumed that the crack retains its shape until the moment of failure. Where σ_1 and σ_3 are tensile or where the rock is competent and not too highly stressed, this would be expected. In an incompetent or highly stressed rock containing flat cracks, allowance may have to be made for the closure of the crack before failure and the introduction of the internal friction coefficient μ equal to $1/\tan 2\alpha$ into the analysis. McClintock and Walsh

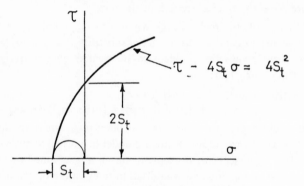

Figure 5.8   Griffith envelope.

(1962) have analysed this departure from the Griffith criterion, arriving at a criterion for failure of a closed crack in the form:

$$4S_T = [(\sigma_1 - \sigma_3)(1 + \mu^2)^{\frac{1}{2}}] - \mu(\sigma_1 + \sigma_3) \qquad (5.33)$$

This criterion may be represented by a straight-line Mohr envelope of the form:

$$\tau = \mu\sigma + 2S_T \qquad (5.34)$$

yielding a curve identical with the Coulomb–Navier envelope.

The Griffith criterion of tensile failure can therefore be used to arrive at similar conclusions to those of the Mohr and Coulomb–Navier criteria for competent rocks. It is, however, of little use in incompetent rocks. The actual mechanism of failure in rock is still the subject of hypothesis but it seems possible that triaxial failure in shear may involve failure along cracks – either large cracks of known orientation along bedding or joint planes (this is discussed further in Chapter 10) or smaller cracks associated with the granular structure of the rock. The significance of this may be demonstrated in a markedly anisotropic rock which will tend to fail more quickly in one direction than another. It will also explain discrepancies often found in the failure angle α encountered in a rock mass, which is often less than that found in a triaxial test on a rock specimen.

It must however be stated that despite this practical justification and its theoretical elegance, there can be little general application of the Griffith failure criterion to rocks – basically because the changing properties of rock require an empirical approach as represented by the Mohr or Coulomb–Navier criteria of failure. The Griffith criterion applied to rock is at best a rather complicated way of arriving at a logical solution.

6

Dynamic Properties of Rocks

So far the properties of rocks have been considered only from the point of view of their reaction to static stresses – the stresses to which a structure in rock would normally be subjected. However, in its construction stages – and possibly later if earthquakes or nuclear explosions are considered – a rock may be subject to transient dynamic loading from the action of explosives, often exceeding by many orders of magnitude any static stresses to which it may be subjected. The way in which a rock may accept or reject these dynamic stresses is of fundamental importance to the design of structures in rock. In particular the ability of a rock to withstand high dynamic stresses without failure has wide importance.

A dynamic load is defined basically by the speed of its action and its ability to initiate shock and/or stress waves in a rock. Thus a load applied over a period of seconds while theoretically dynamic in its application would not create in a rock a stress situation radically different from that induced by a static load. A hammer blow or explosion, on the other hand, applied over a period of microseconds, will initiate complex stresses and probably shock, plastic and elastic waves in the rock.

6.1 Wave Propagation in a Rock Mass

When an explosive is detonated in intimate contact with a rock body, the instantaneous pressures generated can vary from approximately 50,000 kg/cm² to several million kg/cm², depending on the type and quantity of explosive involved and its velocity of detonation. Some of the energy transmitted from the explosive to the rock does work in pulverizing or melting the rock in the immediate vicinity of the impact point whilst the remaining shock energy passes directly into the rock body in an unstable compressive shock front travelling at a speed greater than the sonic velocity of the rock.

A true *shock* wave is only formed when the initial explosive pressure so far exceeds the strength of the rock in compression that any plastic state is by-passed and it can be said to behave hydrodynamically. In other words the pressure state in a rock simulates that in a liquid (Farmer and Attewell, 1963).

Such an unstable shock wave rapidly passes through the non-elastic state due to its instability and decreasing velocity (Attewell and Farmer, 1964) and settles into a stable quasi-elastic zone in which the oscillatory wave motion – propagating at sonic velocity – carries insufficient energy permanently to disturb the material in its path. This zone is known as the *elastic* or *seismic* wave zone.

There are two basic types of elastic wave: *body waves* which travel through the interior of the rock body, and *surface waves* which can only travel along the surface of the material. Body waves can be subdivided into two modes: *compression* or primary (P) waves and *shear* or secondary (S) waves. P-waves induce longitudinal oscillatory particle motions similar in many ways to simple harmonic vibrations and when they impinge on a free boundary in any direction other than head-on, one of the resultant effects of the displacement is the induction of S-waves in which the particles move in a transverse direction without compressing the material. P-waves, of course, travel in any direction in a material which resists compression, but since S-waves depend upon the ability

RATE OF CHANGE IN LENGTH OF SIDE (l_x) :

$$\frac{\partial u}{\partial x} = \frac{\Delta l_x}{l_x} = \frac{1}{E}\left[\sigma_x - \nu(\sigma_y + \sigma_z)\right]$$

similarly, $\dfrac{\partial v}{\partial x} = \dfrac{\Delta l_y}{l_y}$, $\dfrac{\partial w}{\partial x} = \dfrac{\Delta l_z}{l_z}$

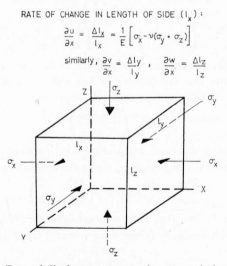

Figure 6.1   Rate of displacement around a stressed elemental cube.

F

of the transmitting material to resist changes in shape, they can only exist in a solid.

The velocity equations of these waves can be deduced by letting u, v, w be the displacement of particles in the x-, y- and z-directions (Figure 6.1) and by showing, as a result of combining Newton's laws of motion with the theory of elasticity, that the general equations of motion for an isotropic, elastic solid are (Howell, 1959):

in the x-direction $$\rho\frac{\partial^2 u}{\partial t^2} = \left(K + \frac{G}{3}\right)\frac{\partial \Delta}{\partial x} + Gu\nabla^2 + \rho X \qquad (6.1)$$

in the y-direction $$\rho\frac{\partial^2 v}{\partial t^2} = \left(K + \frac{G}{3}\right)\frac{\partial \Delta}{\partial y} + Gv\nabla^2 + \rho Y \qquad (6.2)$$

in the z-direction $$\rho\frac{\partial^2 w}{\partial t^2} = \left(K + \frac{G}{3}\right)\frac{\partial \Delta}{\partial z} + Gw\nabla^2 + \rho Z \qquad (6.3)$$

where K, G are respectively the bulk modulus and modulus of rigidity,

ρ is the density,

Δ is the volumetric strain,

ρX, ρY, ρZ are body forces

and ∇^2 is the Laplacian operator:

$$\nabla^2 = \frac{\partial^2}{\partial x^2} + \frac{\partial^2}{\partial y^2} + \frac{\partial^2}{\partial z^2}$$

Differentiating eqn (6.1) with respect to x, eqn (6.2) with respect to y and eqn (6.3) with respect to z gives on summing

$$\frac{\partial^2 \Delta}{\partial t^2} = \left(\frac{K + \frac{4}{3}G}{\rho}\right)\Delta\nabla^2 + \rho\left(\frac{\partial X}{\partial x} + \frac{\partial Y}{\partial y} + \frac{\partial Z}{\partial z}\right) \qquad (6.4)$$

which simplifies for constant body forces to the *wave equation*, from which it follows that compression waves will propagate through an elastic body with velocity C_p numerically equal to:

$$C_p = \left(\frac{K + \frac{4}{3}G}{\rho}\right)^{\frac{1}{2}} \qquad (6.5)$$

If the process is repeated, considering this time only eqns (6.2) and (6.3), the rotational component ω_x about the x-axis may be obtained:

$$\frac{\partial^2 \omega_x}{\partial x^2} = \frac{G}{\rho}\omega_x\nabla^2 + \rho\left(\frac{\partial Y}{\partial y} + \frac{\partial Z}{\partial z}\right) \qquad (6.6)$$

from which it follows that with constant body forces the rotation is transmitted with a velocity (shear wave velocity) C_s equal to

$$C_s = \left(\frac{G}{\rho}\right)^{\frac{1}{2}} \qquad (6.7)$$

Thus the existence and velocity of all elastic waves in a material is a function of its density (ρ) and elasticity and by substitution from eqns (3.11) and (3.12), C_p, C_s can be obtained in terms of the modulus of elasticity E and Poisson's ratio ν.

$$C_p = \left[\frac{E(1 - \nu)g}{\rho(1 + \nu)(1 - 2\nu)}\right]^{\frac{1}{2}} \qquad (6.8)$$

and

$$C_s = \left[\frac{Eg}{2\rho(1 + \nu)}\right]^{\frac{1}{2}} \qquad (6.9)$$

In this case E represents the *dynamic modulus* of elasticity mentioned in Chapter 3 as the dynamic equivalent of the *static modulus* at zero confinement and g is the acceleration due to gravity.

Thus, if the rock were elastic and it could be assumed that ν had a constant value of 0·25 and ρ an approximate constant value of 2·6 gm/cc for all rocks, there should be a consistent relationship between C_p and C_s and E (kg/cm²) in the form:

$$C_p = 1\cdot1\left(\sqrt{\frac{Eg}{\rho}}\right) = 6\cdot8\sqrt{(E)} \text{ m/sec} \qquad (6.10)$$

$$C_s = 0\cdot63\sqrt{\left(\frac{Eg}{\rho}\right)} = 3\cdot9\sqrt{(E)} \text{ m/sec} \qquad (6.11)$$

giving a velocity ratio $C_p/C_s = 1\cdot73$.

This is the basis of the test for determining the *dynamic* modulus of elasticity (Section 7.4).

There is in fact a strong similarity between experimental results and eqns (6.10) and (6.11), Brown and Robertshaw (1953) and Judd and Huber (1962) demonstrating a distinct curvilinear relationship between C_p and E in the form $C_p \propto E^{0.4}$ (Figure 6.2a) and various workers

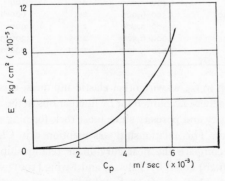

Figure 6.2 (a)

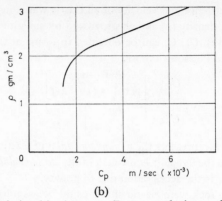

(b)

Figure 6.2 Relationship between P-wave velocity and (a) dynamic modulus of elasticity (after Talwani and Ewing) and (b) density (after Judd and Huber).

(Nicholls, 1961; Davies, Farmer and Attewell, 1964) estimating C_p/C_s in the region of 1·6–1·7. Typical values of C_p are listed in Table 6.1.

TABLE 6.1   Typical P-wave Velocities

Rock	C_p (m/sec)	ρ (gm/cc)	ρC_p (kg/cm²–sec)
Granite	3,000–5,000	2·65	800–1,300
Basalt	4,500–6,500	2·85	1,300–1,800
Dolerite	4,500–6,500	3·0	1,350–1,950
Gabbro	4,500–6,500	3·05	1,400–2,000
Sandstone	1,400–4,000	2·55	350–1,000
Shale	1,400–3,000	2·3	300– 700
Limestone	2,500–6,000	2·5	600–1,500
Marble	3,500–6,000	2·65	900–1,600
Quartzite	5,000–6,500	2·65	1,300–1,650
Slate	3,500–5,500	2·65	900–1,450

The variation in C_p, as with other elastic and quasi-elastic properties of rock, can largely be accounted for by fluctuations in the rock structure and hence density and porosity since most rock-forming minerals have similar densities. This relationship was mentioned in Chapter 3. It is interesting to compare the near-curvilinear relationship between C_p and ρ (Figure 6.2b) noted by Talwani and Ewing (1961) with the near-linear relationship between C_p and ρ noted by Judd and Weber (1961).

Unless an explosion is deep-seated and in highly homogeneous rock, body waves normally carry less than half the energy released by the explosion, the remainder being carried by *surface waves* which travel along surfaces or interfaces in the rock. Surface waves have been subdivided into four modes of which two – *Rayleigh* (R) waves and *Love* (Q) waves – are reasonably easily detected and identified and two – *Hydrodynamic* (H) waves and *Coupled* (C) waves – are of somewhat dubious origin.

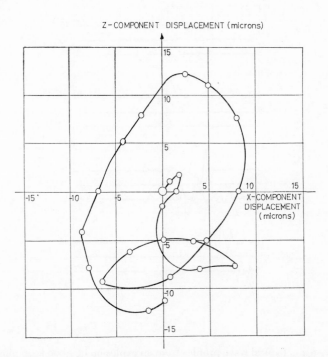

Figure 6.3 R-wave orbit. Time interval between points, 0·0025 sec. (After Davies, Farmer and Attewell.)

A particle subject to an R-wave disturbance follows an elliptical path in retrograde motion and involves no displacement in shear (Figure 6.3). It is in other words similar to the P-wave, while the Q-wave which oscillates in a transverse direction is similar to the S-wave. The velocity of the R-wave can be calculated (Knopoff, 1953) for a Poisson's ratio of 0·25, as equal to 0·92C_s while the Q-wave velocity is approximately equal to C_s. In fact the R-wave velocity C_R is rather less than this, being approximately equal to half the P-wave velocity. Figure 6.4 demonstrates the position of each of the four major waves arriving at a series of gauges placed in the x-, y- and z-directions. The P and R waves are detected in the x- and z- (vertical plane) directions and the transverse S and Q waves in the y-direction only.

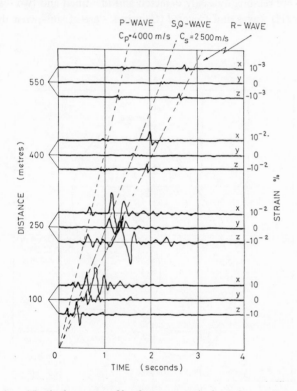

Figure 6.4   Typical wave profiles from an explosion of 1,000 kg explosive in granite.

6.2 Oscillatory Wave Motion in Rock

An oscillatory seismic elastic wave in rock takes a form similar to that of simple harmonic motion, the wave being defined in terms of frequency (f) and wavelength (L) (where $L = C_p/f$) and the amplitude of particle displacement (A_d). A_d can be related to the corresponding velocity of particle displacement V_d through the frequency:

$$v_d = 2\pi f A_d \tag{6.12}$$

where A_d is the displacement of rock in the wavepath initiated in all directions by the energy content of the wave pulse.

V_d is a more useful indicator of rock movement in the wave path in practice, since it can be related directly to stress and strain levels in the wave motion:

$$\sigma = \rho C_p V_d \qquad (6.13)$$

$$\varepsilon = \frac{C_p}{V_d} \qquad (6.14)$$

where the constant factor in eqn (6.10) is ignored. This would not be a satisfactory approximation in the case of the shear wave.

Since V_d is independent of frequency it also represents the differential (dA_d/dt) rather than the actual displacement of the material – a critical factor where structures are encountered.

It must be remembered that eqns (6.13) and (6.14) represent the stress level in a body wave. In a surface (R) wave, despite the fact that the velocity is halved, the particle velocity of the wave is nearly doubled; thus for the same conditions the stress level is unchanged:

$$\sigma = \rho C_R V_d \qquad (6.15)$$

Neither the frequency nor the velocity of particle displacement of the wave are constant. Both decrease with distance from source and the initial magnitude of both is determined by the initial magnitude of the energy released at the wave source. The rate of attenuation of both frequency and velocity of particle displacement is a complex function of the mechanical and geological properties of the rock traversed and the distance travelled by the wave.

An elastic wave will be supported more efficiently by rocks whose properties approximate nearest to those of elastic materials, but will lose energy rapidly in unconsolidated or weak materials. On the other hand the displacement of weak materials for a given wave energy will be far greater than the displacement of a strong rock. Thus constant factors relating frequency and particle velocity to source energy and distance are liable to vary considerably with prevailing geological conditions. However there is evidence to suggest that a divergent spherical P-wave propagated into an infinite homogeneous and isotropic elastic or visco-elastic solid will show reduced velocity of particle displacement in proportion to r^{-3} close to the wave source (shock and plastic wave) reducing to r^{-1} at greater distances, where r is the radial distance of the wave front from the source. In practice it is difficult to separate the two zones but results suggest that in the limited shock and plastic wave zones close to the source, the −3 exponent is roughly correct (Atchison and Roth, 1961; Atchison and Tournay, 1959) while in the general elastic zone an exponent in the region of −2 is more acceptable (Duval *et al.*, 1962; Davies *et al.*, 1964).

Thus for a P-wave, the attenuation of particle velocity will be proportional to r^{-2} over a wide range of distances.

For the same range, the decrease of frequency with distance takes an approximately inverse form. The frequency range of seismic waves covers the range 10^{-3}–10 c/s.

The rate of displacement attenuation for a shear wave is rather less than for the P-wave – since the initial displacement magnitude is rather less – being roughly proportional to $r^{-1.5}$. There is, however, no distinguishable difference in frequency between the two waves.

6.3 Stress and Strain in Waves

The previous sections have introduced the concept of a stable shock front decaying to form an oscillating elastic wave, which in a rock mass will emanate spherically from an explosion or other source of dynamic energy release. The wave, whether shock or elastic, passing a point in a rock will take the form of a stress pulse (compression or shear) of finite and brief duration. In design of structures, the magnitude of this stress pulse is of primary importance, and since this is related to the velocity of particle displacement in the wave front, its magnitude depends primarily on the two displacement/frequency attenuation parameters – the amount of energy transmitted to the rock from the source of the wave and the distance of the point from the source.

The amount of energy transmitted from the source can vary widely. In the case of an explosion it depends largely on the matching of the *characteristic impedance* (or specific acoustic resistance) of the explosive and the surrounding rock. The characteristic impedance is the product of the density and wave velocity (or detonation velocity), ρC_p (Table 6.1), so in the case of hard rock where the rock/explosive impedance ratio approaches unity, transfer of energy will be high, whereas if a layer of air with low impedance comes between the explosive and the rock, transfer will be low. In cases of strain energy release from rock-bursts and earthquakes it is difficult to estimate the energy transmitted.

The effect of the distance of the wave from its source on the stress magnitude can be analysed rather more exactly. It has already been shown that the stress in any constrained wave motion attenuates or 'damps' with time and distance. For the shock wave the reducing stress in the wave can be expressed in the Hugonot equation:

$$\sigma = \frac{\rho v^2}{g}\left(1 - \frac{\rho}{\rho_s}\right) \qquad (6.16)$$

where v is the reducing shock-wave velocity, ρ_s is the density of the rock in the shock-wave front, and the term $\rho v^2/g$ is approximately equivalent to the instantaneous shock modulus of elasticity.

Obviously it is impracticable to measure ρ_s, but it can be shown (Selberg, 1952) that eqn (6.16) follows an exponential form which can be restated empirically as:

$$\sigma = K'\frac{\rho v^2}{g}\frac{r_0}{r}\exp\left(-\alpha'\frac{r}{r_0}\right) \qquad (6.17)$$

where r is the radial distance from the source, r_0 is the radius of the assumed spherical explosive source, directly proportional to the cube root of its weight, W.

K', α' are constants proportional to the *propagation* and *absorption* constants, K, α.

For a compressive elastic wave under elastic conditions, v becomes equal to C_p and eqn (6.17) can be reduced to:

$$\varepsilon = K\frac{W^{\frac{1}{3}}}{r}\exp -\alpha\frac{r}{W^{\frac{1}{3}}} \qquad (6.18)$$

This is the *wave propagation law* of Duvall and Petkoff (1959), who have shown that in most rocks $\alpha = 0\cdot3$ and K is roughly inversely proportional to E having values ranging from 2,000 to 3,000 m/kg$^{\frac{1}{3}}$ for rocks with high moduli of elasticity to 1,000 to 1,500 m/kg$^{\frac{1}{3}}$ for rocks with low moduli of elasticity. As mentioned previously however, such constants must be treated with caution.

The wave propagation law can also be expressed in the simpler forms (Duvall *et al.*, 1962; Attewell, Farmer and Haslam, 1965) mentioned previously and related directly to distance

$$\varepsilon = \frac{K}{C_p}\left(\frac{W}{r^2}\right)^n = \frac{V_d}{C_p} \qquad (6.19)$$

or

$$\varepsilon = \frac{K}{v}\left(\frac{W}{r^3}\right)^n \qquad (6.20)$$

where eqn (6.19) represents seismic wave attentuation and eqn (6.20) shock wave decay. K and n represent *site factors*, where n can often be taken as unity and K varies widely with depth, wave direction, strata conditions and direction. In particular, K can vary widely with wave direction if the wave motion is elliptical in form, when the vertical displacement (z-direction) (and hence K) may be three or four times as great as the horizontal displacement (x-direction), while the horizontal displacement may itself be less than the shear displacement. The order of K in eqn (6.19) is however in the region of 1 m³/kg-sec.

An important factor in any consideration of wave motion is the extent of the shock plastic wave zone with its high, rapidly decaying compression front. Rinehart (1961) suggests that the limit to the zone may be approximately fixed at $10r_0$ – ten times the initial source radius in the case of a spherical explosive source, and probably rather less in the case of a cylindrical source, where Selberg suggests that eqn (6.18) may be re-written:

$$\varepsilon = K \sqrt{\left(\frac{r_0}{r}\right)} \exp\left(-\alpha\frac{r}{r_0}\right) \tag{6.21}$$

This means that the direct shattering effect of any dynamic wave is limited, since outside the shock/plastic zone, stress levels may be assumed to fall below the compressive strength of the rock. It also means that since the duration of pulse is low, time-dependent effects outside this zone can be ignored, and since inside the zone, fracturing is comprehensive, flow effects at the high stresses involved have little practical significance unless high temperatures are attained in the detonation process. Dynamic effects in rock can at most sub-nuclear explosive levels therefore be considered solely in relation to brittle failure, dependent on the stress level in the wave, and since the major part of the wave has a stress level sufficiently low to eliminate compressive failure, tensile effects in reflected waves must be considered.

6.4 Reflection of Stress Waves

When a wave strikes an interface in its travel through rock, represented by a joint, bed, fault or free surface, part of the wave energy is transmitted and part of the wave energy is reflected. The reflected and transmitted parts of the wave are a function of the characteristic impedance of the rock on each side of the interface and for normal incidence may be represented:

$$\sigma_R = \frac{\rho_2 C_{p_2} - \rho_1 C_{p_1}}{\rho_1 C_{p_1} + \rho_2 C_{p_2}}\sigma_i \tag{6.22}$$

$$\sigma_T = \frac{2\rho_2 C_{p_2}}{\rho_1 C_{p_1} + \rho_2 C_{p_2}}\sigma_i \tag{6.23}$$

where the suffixes i, T, R, refer to the incident, transmitted and reflected parts of the wave and the suffixes 1, 2 refer to the two media, the wave travelling from 1 to 2. It can be seen for an incident compression wave therefore that if $\rho_1 C_{p_1} = \rho_2 C_{p_2}$ then $\sigma_R = 0$ and $\sigma_T = \sigma_i$ and there is therefore no loss across the interface; if $\rho_2 C_{p_2} > \rho_1 C_{p_1}$ there will be a transmitted compression wave and a reflected compression wave; if $\rho_1 C_{p_1} > \rho_2 C_{p_2}$ there will be a transmitted compressive wave and a reflected tensile wave and if $\rho_2 C_{p_2} = 0$ (the case of a free surface in air) then $\sigma_T = 0$, $\sigma_R = -\sigma_i$ and there will be a fully reflected tension wave.

In the latter case, therefore, since rocks have a low tensile strength, an elastic wave could cause serious damage to a structure in rock, particularly in the complex stress zone formed by a reflected tensile wave encountering the edge of the oncoming compression wave.

Where a stress wave meets an oblique surface a rather different picture emerges and it is necessary to consider, apart from the reflected and transmitted (refracted) waves, an induced shear wave into which part of the energy from the wave passes. At a free face (rock/air), important in design as distinct from geophysical work, stress in the waves will be given by (Rinehart and Pearson, 1953):

$$\sigma_R = B\sigma_i \qquad (6.24)$$

$$\tau = [(B + 1) \cot 2\beta]\sigma_i \qquad (6.25)$$

where
$$B = \frac{\tan \beta \tan^2 2\beta - \tan \alpha}{\tan \beta \tan^2 2\beta + \tan \alpha}$$

and
$$\sin \beta = \sin \alpha \left(\frac{1 - 2\nu}{2(1 - \nu)}\right)^{\frac{1}{2}}$$

Where refraction is involved at a rock/rock interface the relative stresses transmitted and reflected are given by eqns (6.24) and (6.25); they are in other words only affected by the material properties. The angle of refraction (R) is given by Snell's law as in optics, i.e.

$$\sin R = \sin i \, (C_{p_1}/C_{p_2})$$

6.5 Dynamic Strength of Rocks

Rocks can resist a higher magnitude of dynamic load than of static load. Some comparative values are quoted in Table 6.2 (Rinehart, 1964) which show that in all cases the dynamic strength is from five to ten times the static strength of the same rock – probably nearer five for stronger rocks and ten for weaker rocks.

It is evident, therefore, that failure predictions based on dynamic stress or a combination of static and dynamic stresses applied to a structure must be carefully evaluated.

The reason for the large increase in strength under dynamic loading conditions – and there is no reason to believe that this strength increase does not progress with rate of loading – must lie in the transient nature of the stress pulse and its localized area of immediate action, meaning that failure mechanisms in the rock which have been shown previously to be time-dependent, whatever their nature, are incapable of completion during the duration of the pulse. It must be remembered, however, that in any structure subject to a large number of transient stresses (particularly of high magnitude) there must be danger of *fatigue* failure. The values quoted in Table 6.2 refer, therefore, to a single transient stress pulse. For a series of such pulses it may be that the static strength is a more realistic failure parameter.

TABLE 6.2   Dynamic Tensile Strength of Rock (kg/cm²)

Rock	Static	Dynamic	Ratio
Granite	70	390	5·7
Taconite	70	900	13·0
Limestone	40	280	6·5
Marble	60	480	7·8

The difficulty in defining dynamic strength exactly for practical purposes, often leads to quotation of a readily reproducible standard test result which can be compared with static strength parameters for rock. Any of the standard pendulum impact testing procedures used on metals can be adapted for this purpose, provided a standard test specimen is used; the value for *impact toughness* being given in kg-m/cm³, or energy/unit volume crushed. This can be converted to kg/cm², giving a value which can readily be compared with static strength values.

The usefulness of the test (see Chapter 7) is limited by the dependance of impact toughness on the shape of the specimen exposed to impact. The test is therefore purely comparative and results must be related to a known static strength property. Figure 6.5 shows a tentative relationship for cylindrical specimens 2·5 cm diameter and 2·5 cm long (impact width). This is roughly curvilinear suggesting that resistance to dynamic loading is less pronounced in stronger, more brittle rocks. This is particularly important since it agrees with tentative conclusions of many workers that there is a similar relationship between *scleroscope hardness* and static strength (Greenland, 1961; Judd and Huber, 1961), suggesting that dynamic strength is related to hardness and hence *surface energy* (Terichow and Larson, 1967) rather than conventional rock strength parameters. This is important inasmuch as it has already been shown that by reducing surface energy by chemical means (Rehbinder *et al.*, 1948) the impact resistance of a rock is appreciably reduced. The implications of this in drilling and rock fracture practice are wide.

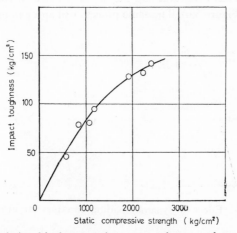

Figure 6.5 Relationship between impact toughness and static strength.

6.6 Deformation Processes under Dynamic Loading

If it is accepted that rocks can resist dynamic loads well in excess of the equivalent static load, it is evident that there must also be differences in the mechanism of deformation. The basic mechanism of dynamic deformation in rock may be considered by comparison with static deformation of a competent rock – where compressive loading will induce a near-linear (quasi-elastic) stress/strain relationship. In a perfectly elastic material induced strain will be instantaneous; in a rock where strain is caused by interatomic movement and movement along grain boundaries and weaknesses, deformation will be a time-dependent process, causing a lag of strain behind stress. This anelastic effect, in materials subject to cyclic stress (vibration), is responsible for internal damping or attenuation – the decay in the amplitude of a wave and hence the dissipation of energy, usually in the form of heat. (This process is often equated to internal friction.)

The major difference between dynamic and static loading can be best seen in terms of the *thermoelastic after-effect*, a reversal of the normal process of thermal expansion. This means that (except under high levels of hydrostatic loading) when a body is loaded statically and it expands or contracts, there will be a slight heat loss or gain by the body material which will be equalized by thermal transfer from the surrounding material. In other words, under static loading conditions the temperature will remain constant and the strain (change in volume) will be *isothermal* (Figure 6.6). The same process will apply to unloading.

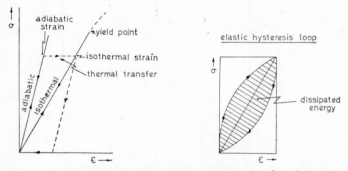

Figure 6.6   Effect of dynamic loading on stress/strain relationship.

On the other hand, if the material is loaded dynamically, that is, at such a rate that thermal transfer is impossible, the temperature of the material will rise or fall and expansion or contraction will be adiabatic. In other words, for the same stress there will be considerably less strain (Figure 6.6), which if the load is instantaneously removed will revert to zero along the same path, losing or gaining in temperature in the process. If the load is maintained, however, then as the temperature regains its normal level, the strain will increase to static levels – a similar adiabatic expansion/contraction and slow recovery occurring on the removal of the load. In a cyclic process the adiabatic deformation and recovery combine to form a hysteresis loop, the area of which is equivalent to the energy dissipated in the cycle.

It is not surprising, therefore, since failure is dependent on the magnitude of deformation that a material will withstand high transient stresses and that the strength of the material depends largely on the duration of the stress, which will be minimal in most cases of dynamic loading encountered in rock engineering. Thus a quasi- or semi-elastic rock, apart from having a high dynamic strength, should also have a proportionately high dynamic modulus of elasticity. This is revealed to a certain extent in the dynamic tests for elastic moduli which yield a modulus of elasticity rather larger than that at zero static stress (Sutherland, 1963). The difference is normally in the region of 25%, although with badly controlled laboratory tests it may be higher.

In non-elastic rocks whose deformation is primarily viscous the same effect is noticed under dynamic loading, the total strain decreasing in proportion to the rate of loading. Since the strain in these rocks is in any case time-dependent, however, the effect under dynamic conditions is less apparent than in semi-brittle rocks.

7
Rock Testing

In previous chapters, mechanical properties of rocks have been defined, discussed and described and in certain instances stated quantitatively. Obviously in a material as inexact and changing as rock, quantitative description has some serious disadvantages, unless the rock in question has been subject to individual tests, which can be devised to define its mechanical properties – basically its elasticity, viscosity, and strength under predetermined environmental conditions.

Unlike the case of structural materials such as steel, concrete or even soils, there are few standardized rock-testing techniques with universal acceptance (cf. Obert *et al.*, 1946; American Society for Testing and Materials, 1966). Accepted techniques are, however, fairly widespread and may be divided roughly into two groups: *laboratory tests* based on the standard one-inch (2·54 cm) diameter core or cylinder of material, obtained from a known site at a known orientation, and *in-situ tests* used to determine directly, if sometimes roughly, mechanical properties under site conditions. The quantitative values quoted previously are the result of laboratory tests. Their relationship to *in-situ* tests is discussed below.

7.1 Laboratory Testing - Specimen Preparation

Most accepted laboratory tests are based on a *one-inch* ($2\frac{1}{2}$ cm) diameter cylindrical core of rock. Provided the rock is not seriously affected by water, this can be obtained either directly from an exploratory drill core or indirectly from a laboratory rock specimen with a diamond coring drill, chuck mounted in a conventional vertical boring machine, rigidly anchored for smooth action and lubricated with water. In rare cases where the rock might be seriously affected by water, dry coring with some form of dust suction or air blower may take rather longer and may induce drill wear, but will be equally effective.

Unless cores are obtained from the actual site, specimens of rock obtained for coring must be marked clearly for position, dip, joint frequency, grain orientation and any other factors which may eventually affect the rock properties in mass, so that the exact orientation of any important features relative to the core axis may be known or controlled. The position of the core axes relative to the directions of principal stress must also be estimated for more involved tests.

The faces of the core (length will depend to a certain extent on the type of test) must be exactly at right angles to the core axis and must be flat and smooth (deviations can cause considerable error) and the core itself should be either *artificially dried* or totally *saturated*, since water content (see Chapter 8) at room temperature can vary in proportion to porosity, humidity and the original degree of saturation. The smoothness and flatness of the core ends can be obtained to a satisfactory degree by use of a lapping machine consisting of a horizontal revolving turntable, lubricated with wet carborundum upon which the cores are allowed to stand freely.

A satisfactory core is therefore a smoothly finished cylinder (tolerances depend on the accuracy required, but should not exceed 1 mm) of rock, one inch in diameter from a known position in the rock mass. This last point is particularly important since little can be gained by stressing a rock in a direction in which it is unlikely to be stressed under natural circumstances.

7.2 Laboratory Tests – Stress/Strain Characteristics

An essential item in any rock-testing laboratory is a hydraulic press of some type with a maximum vertical loading level of at least 25 tonnes and a facility for controlling rates of loading. Some method of measuring deformation in the loaded core is also desirable.

With this and a suitable anchoring device for tensile tests the full stress/strain characteristics of a rock specimen under uniaxial loading can be obtained simply by applying a tensile or compressive load along the axis of the specimen at a specified loading rate (normally between 1,000 and 5,000 kg/min depending on the rock strengths but sufficiently low to eliminate dynamic loading effects) and noting the recorded strain. Because anchoring devices tend to create a plane of weakness in the specimen, it is sometimes desirable when conducting direct tensile tests, to machine a length of the core (Figure 7.1) to a reduced diameter.

Since the maximum strain preceding failure is not likely to exceed

G

5%, it is evident that in the conventional core size (5 cm long by $2\frac{1}{2}$ cm diameter) maximum axial and lateral contractions (or extensions) will be around 0·2 cm and 0·03 cm. In all probability they may be rather less than this but nevertheless sufficiently large for accurate physical measurement with strain gauges bonded to the sample and for calculation of the *modulus of elasticity* and *Poisson's ratio*, together with an indication of stress/strain and time/strain characteristics of the rock.

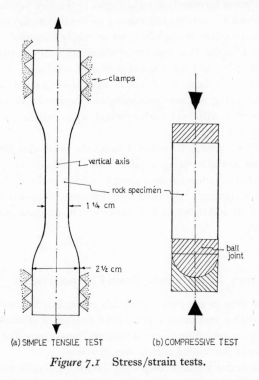

Figure 7.1   Stress/strain tests.

For long-term *creep tests* the time element will preclude the use of expensive laboratory equipment, and in this case some form of simple load magnification can be used, such as a lever loading device (Figure 7.2). Strain gauges, bonded to the specimen, may be used to measure deformation, but over a prolonged period, possible deformation of the strain gauge itself must be considered.

It is desirable in uniaxial stress/strain tests to equate the direction of applied stress in the test specimen to the direction of major principal stress (usually the vertical stress in rock) in any likely application, unless specifically required otherwise. It is also essential that the direction of applied stress be parallel to the axis of the test core. This can be achieved in various ways, but largely depends on the design of loading platens or clamps on the press (Figure 7.1), which must be exactly normal to the direction of load. In compressive tests, ball joints are a useful method of ensuring verticality.

A further simple method of determining the elastic constants in a rock makes use of its *dynamic* properties, giving values of the dynamic constants. Based on a standard concrete test the apparatus consists basically of an electromagnetic driver energized by a variable-frequency

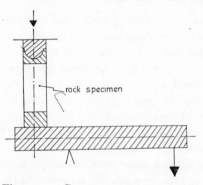

Figure 7.2   Constant stress creep test.

oscillator which is used to vibrate one end of a standard specimen. The amplitude of the vibration at the other end of the specimen reaches a maximum (which can be measured with a vibration pickup) when the frequency (f) of the oscillator is equal to the natural frequency of the specimen and the wavelength of the vibration in the core is equal to one half the length (l) of the specimen. This condition is known as *resonance* and the longitudinal wave velocity at this point is equal to:

$$C_v = 2fl \qquad (7.1)$$

in which case the modulus of elasticity $E \simeq C_v{}^2\dfrac{\rho}{g}$ (7.2)

where ρ is the density of the rock (see eqn 6.10) and Poisson's ratio is assumed to be approximately 0·25.

The value of E obtained in this way is roughly equivalent to the initial tangent modulus under dynamic conditions; it has, however, a natural tendency to be high and the test must be treated with considerable caution. In particular, since the length of the specimen controls frequency and resonance, E measured by this method will be dependent on specimen length. An alternative method using piezoelectric receivers (barium titanate and lead zirconate) can be used to obtain velocity values over a wider frequency range.

From E and v, which are by their definition uniaxial constants and therefore relatively easily obtained, the other elastic constants may be calculated. In the unlikely event of a direct measurement being required, shear or triaxial tests can be adapted to give values for G, λ or K.

7.3 Laboratory Tests – Strength

The most important criterion of mechanical rock reaction is strength. The basic reason for any stress analysis is the prediction of failure – the point at which the applied stress equates to strength; this is the basis of laboratory strength tests. Initially there are three major strength parameters – uniaxial compressive, tensile and shear strength – the value of each being obtained from a one-inch core test.

The conventional *compressive strength* test is virtually identical to the stress/strain compression test taken to failure, except that the length of the core is normally 2·5 cm, equal to the diameter, instead of 5 cm. However, this is not important since the compressive strength (S_c) for any core length (L) can be related to the standard (S_{c_0}) through:

$$S_c = S_{c_0}\left(0{\cdot}8 + \frac{1}{2L}\right) \tag{7.3}$$

based on eqn (5.1), where L is the length of core in centimetres.

The one difficulty in the test is the estimation of the point of failure in weaker rocks. In hard brittle rocks, test failure is dynamic and spectacular. In weaker rocks it is more likely to be heralded by a rapid increase in strain rate.

Tests for *tensile strength* can be based on the tensile stress/strain test. It has, however, been demonstrated that while satisfactory at low stresses there is always a danger of either eccentric loading or weakness planes due to machining, affecting failure levels at high loading rates. A more satisfactory test and one which more nearly simulates actual failure conditions is the *indirect* tensile strength test, sometimes known as the Brazilian test.

The test method (Figure 7.3a) entails diametrical loading of a core so as to induce a uniform tensile stress over the diametrical plane through the core axis. It is essential that the loading platens, apart from being entirely parallel, be sufficiently hard to resist yield which might induce tangential stresses. Failure should ideally appear as a clean break joining the lines of contact, and the tensile strength will be given by:

$$S_T = \frac{2W}{\pi d L} \qquad (7.4)$$

where W is the applied load (applied at a rate of about 200 kg/min) and d, L are the dimensions of the core.

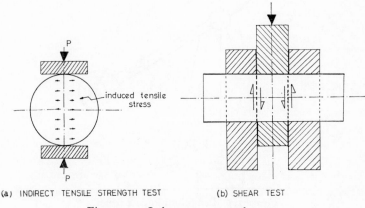

(a) INDIRECT TENSILE STRENGTH TEST   (b) SHEAR TEST

Figure 7.3   Laboratory strength tests.

This test can, in fact, be adapted for use with any shape of specimen, loaded in a similar way and although results tend to be scattered (Hiramatsu and Oka, 1966) they can give a reasonable approximation of tensile strength.

$$S_T = \frac{W}{D^2} \qquad (7.5)$$

where D is the distance between the points of loading – which replaces the loading plane in a core test.

A simple uniaxial *shear strength* test (Figure 7.3b) can be performed by vertical loading of a horizontal core, supported at the ends. The test has unsatisfactory aspects since the core must fit smoothly and exactly into the retaining pieces, and also into the central loading piece for perfect results. The shear strength is given by half the breaking load divided by the core area since there are two shear fracture planes.

If the core is loaded axially this test may be adapted (Ortlepp, 1960) to give strengths in confinement. However, it is likely that, under such circumstances, the stresses on the failure plane would be difficult to analyse or adapt to any likely failure circumstances.

Impact testing to simulate dynamic failure is as yet rarely applied to rocks. Any type of pendulum impact tester (Figure 7.4) can be readily adapted to give values of *impact toughness* (I_T) where:

$$I_T = \frac{E}{La}\,\text{kg/cm}^2 \qquad (7.5)$$

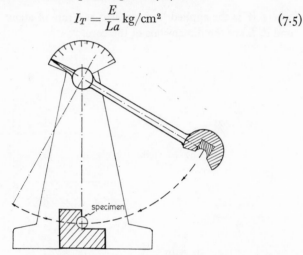

Figure 7.4   Pendulum impact tester.

where E is the energy in the pendulum at impact, L is the length of the specimen, and a is the cross-sectional area of the specimen.

In this context there are numerous *hardness* and *penetration* tests, widely used in metallurgical testing, which have at various times been applied to rocks. These are particularly useful as rapid laboratory or *in-situ* tests, but considerable care is required in relating data obtained from them to conventional rock strength criteria.

7.4 Triaxial Testing

Values of the uniaxial compressive, tensile and shear strength can give an adequate representation of rock properties under unconfined load conditions and may be used to estimate properties under confinement. The purpose of the triaxial test is to determine the reaction of rock specimens to confining pressures similar to those found in the earth's stress field. Ideally this would entail the confinement of a cubic or rectangular block of rock subject to different pressures on each face equivalent to the principal stresses in the rock. In fact, because it is so

commonly assumed that the intermediate and minor principal stresses
in the earth's crust are equal, the standard triaxial test is performed on a
cylindrical specimen (one-inch core) loaded axially to simulate the
major principal stress and radially to simulate the minor principal stress.
The essential features of a triaxial test apparatus for rock are shown in
Figure 7.5.

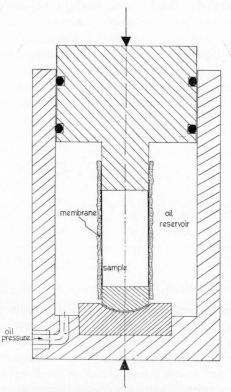

Figure 7.5 Triaxial test apparatus.

The specimen, normally artificially dried at 105–110°C and enclosed
in a heavy rubber (latex) membrane, is loaded axially through a piston
and laterally through the fluid reservoir surrounding it. The dimensions of the specimen are normally 5 cm long by 2·5 cm diameter, the
rubber membrane preventing seepage of hydraulic oil from the reservoir into the pores of the specimen. Where circumstances require a
fully saturated specimen, it should be treated with the liquid concerned (water) in a vacuum desiccator. In the case of a saturated speci-

men it may also be desirable to include an outlet in the cell base for measurement or relief of pore-water pressure.

The axial piston load is normally applied by placing the test cell on the hydraulic press, which is then operated in the same way as for a uniaxial compressive test. The lateral pressure is transmitted through the hydraulic oil by means of a small hydraulic pump. The range of pressures required to simulate most loading conditions encountered in rock engineering require a confining pressure up to 1,000 kg/cm^2 and an axial pressure up to 4,000 kg/cm^2. For this range of pressures and for pressures which would be required for investigation of various rock properties under high confinement, carefully designed test cylinder and fittings are required. For confining pressures in excess of 2,000 kg/cm^2, specially developed seals and fittings will be needed.

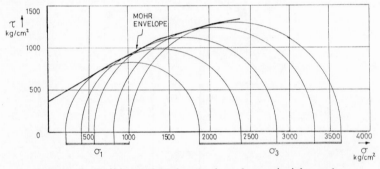

Figure 7.6   Build-up of Mohr envelope from triaxial test data.

The triaxial test apparatus can be used for virtually all rock tests in compression with the exception of lateral strain measurements. Basically it can be used (i) to measure stress/strain characteristics at various confining pressures by noting the movement of the vertical piston, (ii) to measure time/strain characteristics at fixed vertical and lateral stresses by use of bonded strain gauges and (iii) to determine failure at various stress differentials. The latter use is the most common and can be used to build up Mohr or Griffith failure envelopes for rocks.

A typical rock failure test would be performed on (say) five cylindrical end-lapped artificially dried specimens at different confining pressures, say 200, 400, 600, 800 and 1,000 kg/cm^2. The specimens would each be axially loaded to failure at the different confining pressures and the axial and confining pressure, representing the major (σ_1) and minor (σ_3) principal stresses acting on the specimen plotted on the normal stress abscissa of the shear/normal stress graph. The semicircles joining these points (Figure 7.6) will form the basis for a failure envelope tangential to each.

Failures under triaxial test are generally in accord with the Coulomb–Navier or Mohr criteria, following a failure angle $\alpha = 45° + \phi$ to the major principal plane. It is, however, likely that preferential weakness planes (foliation) may considerably influence the failure in a particular direction. In such a case efforts must be made in core selection to include, where feasible, a test in which the direction of the weakness planes coincides with the Mohr failure direction, thus enabling a failure envelope to be plotted showing any wide differential from optimum conditions (see Chapter 10).

7.5 Field Testing

Laboratory methods of testing are more accurate, cheaper, easier to carry out and intellectually more satisfying than field tests. There is, however, the difficulty that rock properties can change over a small area and a pronounced joint or fault system in a large project may affect rock reactions in a way which could never be estimated by laboratory tests. There are two approaches to this problem: (i) a reliance on laboratory data coupled with extensive geological information (this approach is extended in later chapters) or (ii) the conduct of field tests on the actual site.

Field tests tend to be inaccurate, expensive because of their scale, and limited to the particular set of circumstances prevailing at the time of the test. For instance, all rocks are wet – their water content varying with the amount of ground water, the humidity of the air and probably with the amount of drainage or otherwise induced by the test excavation. Since water can affect rock strength by as much as 50%, it is obviously desirable that water conditions be discounted in any test. On the other hand if water and strata conditions are stable, it is obviously desirable to take them into account during a test rather than allow for them afterwards.

Perhaps the most successful field tests are dynamic rather than static tests, although in surface applications (where they are mainly used) they are affected substantially by topography tending to give somewhat diverse results. Static tests are mainly justifiable where they can be used to present a rough analogy of the structural problem.

Field tests follow roughly the same lines as laboratory tests, although obviously they are limited to tests in compression and shear. The commonest are a *jack* test, *bolt* test, or *seismic* test to obtain elastic constants or stress/strain properties, a *plate* test to obtain strength values and various types of *shear* test for the same type of data evaluation as the triaxial test.

The *jack test* can be performed in any excavation or tunnel of suitable width for the insertion of a hydraulic jack (Figure 7.7). One end of the

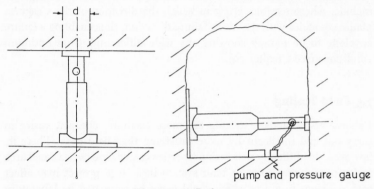

pump and pressure gauge

Figure 7.7   Jack test.

jack must be placed against a continuous surface, such as cured concrete or metal plate, with a large bearing area in contact with the rock wall on the tunnel or trench side, and the other end, which should be a disc of known diameter (d) and relatively small area, must be in intimate contact with the rock on the opposite wall.

Then when a load W is applied to the jack the rock/disc interface will be subject to an applied stress $4W/\pi d^2$ causing a deflection δ, measured by a deflection-measuring device incorporated into the jack. Because of the relative differences in contact area this can be taken as the total deflection at the rock disc contact, and by assuming equal stress in both surface directions, the strain, given by δ/d can be equated to:

$$\varepsilon = \frac{\delta}{d} = \frac{4W(1 - v^2)}{\pi d^2 E} \tag{7.7}$$

This means that to obtain stress/strain characteristics and modulus of elasticity, a value for v must be assumed (say 0·25) giving a relationship in the form:

$$\varepsilon = 0 \cdot 94 \cdot \frac{\sigma}{E}, \quad E = \frac{3 \cdot 76W}{\pi d\delta} \tag{7.8}$$

The jack test may be used for floor/roof, wall/wall surfaces or for virtually any application where pressure can be applied to a rock surface. An adaptation known as the *plate test* uses a rather smaller rock contact disc or piston and the purpose is to fracture the rock rather than deform it. At the point of failure – evident by dynamic fracture or possibly plastic yield – the failure criterion will be a measure of the rock's ability to withstand bearing stresses over a limited area. There is unfortunately no accepted solution to this problem. Perhaps the simplest, suggested by Jenkins (1960) and based on Love's analysis of maximum shearing stress, equates shear strength directly to the load at failure, viz.:

$$S_s = 0{\cdot}35 \cdot \frac{4W}{\pi d^2} \qquad (7.9)$$

(assuming that $v = 0{\cdot}25$).

Analyses based on Mohr's failure theory, however (Prandtl, 1924), suggest a rather lower constant in the region of $0{\cdot}18$, viz.:

$$S_s = 0{\cdot}18 \cdot \frac{4W}{\pi d^2} = 0{\cdot}23 \cdot \frac{W}{d^2} \qquad (7.10)$$

and this is probably a more accurate value.

Where conditions cannot be adapted to suit a jack or plate test, some form of *bolt* test may be feasible. To date, this type of test has only been used in soft rocks (Foote, 1964), but there seems no reason why it should not be extended to medium hard rocks. It consists basically of a standard $0{\cdot}64$-cm ($\frac{1}{4}$-inch) 'Rawlbolt' which is placed in a hole drilled into the rock and expanded. It is then withdrawn forcibly and the load (W) required to break it free measured. This can be related to the shear strength (S_s) of the rock in the following form:

$$S_s = \frac{3W}{\pi h(R + 2r)} \qquad (7.11)$$

where r is the radius of the test hole, and h, R are respectively the length and base radius of the conic crater caused by removal of the bolt (Figure 7.8).

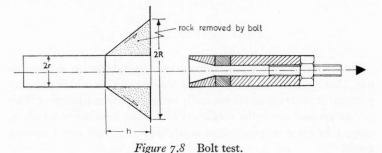

Figure 7.8 Bolt test.

The test is remarkably simple, but of dubious accuracy and small scale. On a larger scale, deformation may be induced in weaker rocks by a stressed cable (up to 100 tonnes) anchored in a borehole (Zienkiewicz and Stagg, 1966, 1967) to give information on rock deformation properties on a macro-scale – an important innovation where feasible.

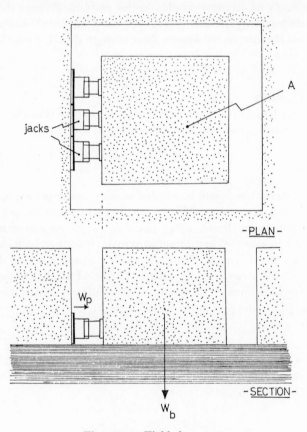

Figure 7.9   Field shear test.

Field *shear tests* are based normally on some adaptation of the plate test. There is, however, a specific type of field shear test which may have practical importance and is not easily simulated in the laboratory. This can be applied where the coefficient of friction between two beds or along a bedding or joint plane is required (see Ruiz and Camargo, 1966).

Basic requirements of this type of test are that a block, including the preferred shear plane, be carefully exposed (Figure 7.9) without use of explosives, on the actual site, either by trenching or tunnelling. It is desirable that several blocks be exposed, where feasible, for repeat tests. A series of hydraulic jacks are then used to apply a shear force across the plane, the normal force being supplied by the weight of the block, or the incumbent strata in the case of a pillar. Deflection gauges are installed to monitor movement along the plane and to differentiate between initial elastic displacement and post-failure slide. Then if the force applied along the plane is W_P and the weight and area of the block are W_B, A, the shear stress (τ) and normal stress (σ) acting on the plane at any one time are equivalent to W_P/A and W_B/A respectively and the failure criterion will be given by:

$$\frac{W_P}{A} = \frac{W_F}{A} + \mu\frac{W_B}{A} \tag{7.12}$$

where W_F/A is the shear stress at failure and μ is the post-failure friction coefficient.

Dynamic elastic constants may be obtained in the field by *seismic tests*. Here a small charge is fired either on the surface or underground and the resulting seismic waves monitored by strain gauges or vibration pickups. It has been shown in Chapter 6 that when a disturbance sets up an elastic wave motion in a rock body, two distinct wave motions are initiated: a stable compressive (P) wave and a rather slower transverse or shear (S) wave. These waves can be separated and their velocities recorded by using gauges set to record in the correct directions (longitudinal for P-waves and lateral for S-waves).

From eqns (6.8) and (6.9) E and ν can be expressed in terms of the respective wave velocities C_p and C_s as:

$$E = \frac{\rho C_s^2}{g}\left[\frac{3(C_p^2/C_s^2) - 4}{(C_p^2/C_s^2) - 1}\right] \tag{7.13}$$

$$\nu = \frac{\frac{1}{2}(C_p^2/C_s^2) - 1}{(C_p^2/C_s^2) - 1} \tag{7.14}$$

Similar expressions can be obtained in terms of K, G and λ. These equations will give dynamic values of E, ν – in other words a modulus equivalent to that at zero load at a confinement depending on the depth of the test. The dynamic value will, however, tend to differ from the equivalent static value due to hysteresis effects. In near-surface tests, site factors – a somewhat dubious assessment of an indeterminate thickness of weathered rock and soil – will also tend to influence results.

7.6 Accuracy of Test Data

It must be accepted that *in-situ* tests are not accurate. The magnitude of the error is unimportant; it may be reduced to reasonable levels by statistical treatment, but *in-situ* tests are normally confined to single rather than multiple measurements. Basically their purpose is a rapid estimation of rock properties where accuracy is not a critical factor (jack and bolt tests) or a careful assessment of a large-scale situation, not amenable to laboratory treatment (shear test).

If any degree of accuracy is required, a relatively large number of carefully controlled tests must be organized, and this can only be accomplished on a small scale in the laboratory. Even here, however, the most sophisticated preparation and measuring techniques will be of little value unless backed by accurate sampling in the first instance, and competent geological evaluation of the final application.

The quotable accuracy of laboratory results depends initially on the number of specimens tested which in turn depends on the money available for testing, and the complexity of the test devised. An important consideration, however, must be the relative homogeneity, continuity and isotropy of the rock under test, and the type of sampling techniques used.

Statistical accuracy is normally quoted in terms of the *standard deviation* (δ) from the *arithmetical mean* of a series of values, viz.:

$$\delta^2 = \frac{1}{n-1} \sum_{x_n}^{x_1} (x - x_a)^2 \qquad (7.15)$$

where n is the number of readings, and x_a is the arithmetical mean of values ranging from x_1 to x_n.

On this basis, from a total of ten samples, a relatively homogeneous, anisotropic rock – such as a fine-grained igneous or fine-grained non-foliated sedimentary rock – will have a standard deviation of from 3% to 10% in strength and elasticity tests depending on the accuracy of the test, while an inhomogeneous, isotropic rock – say a porphyritic granite or a well-foliated sedimentary or metamorphic rock – will have a standard deviation of from 10% to 20% in the same tests, or possibly larger if foliation is particularly pronounced and samples are taken in every direction. Triaxial and creep tests are not amenable to statistical analysis, due to the considerable time factor involved.

The deviation may be reduced if the number of readings taken is greater than ten, when the significance of individual values may be considered. If the number of readings is much lower than ten (say two or three) there is little point in quoting deviation; under such circumstances accuracy will depend largely upon the confidence and experience of the test operator. Under most circumstances this will suffice, for the techniques of design in rock have not yet progressed to the point where strict accuracy is a critical consideration.

8

Effect of Water
on Rock Properties

Rock properties evaluated in the previous chapters have concerned rocks in the dry state. This reflects a frequent assumption in design in rock that either (i) all rocks are dry or (ii) rock properties are unaffected by the presence of pore-water. It has already been shown that rocks are porous, and it is therefore evident that, in their natural state, rocks may contain large quantities of water, sometimes at significant pressures, and since this water in the pore space fills space occupied by air in the dry state, without any structural alteration, it would seem logical that some of the rock properties will be affected. For instance, the density of water is much greater than air, so the apparent density of the rock will be increased; the sonic velocity in water is much greater than in air and its substitution will increase the velocity and hence the magnitude of wave propagation in the rock.

The effects on elasticity, flow, and strength properties are less obvious, but nevertheless significant. They devolve on the relative incompressibility of pore-water when compared with air. The presence of an incompressible pore-fluid under stress means that many of the normal processes of movement in the rock are inhibited, tending to reduce elasticity and strength and to increase flow. The total difference between dry and wet rock properties is thus determined initially by the porosity, permeability and saturation of the rock.

8.1 Flow of Water through Rocks

Porosity (Chapter 1) defines the pore space in a rock as a ratio of the total volume. *Permeability* expresses the ability of the rock to transmit water (or any liquid). The two are closely related and have been equated by Casagrande in the form (Terzaghi and Peck, 1948):

$$p \propto n_a{}^2 \tag{8.1}$$

where p is the coefficient of permeability and n_a is the apparent porosity of the rock.

All materials are permeable, and although most work on permeability concerns the softer rocks and soil, flow of water through all permeable media follows similar laws, based on D'Arcy's pipe-flow law, and taking the form:

$$\frac{Q}{A} = p\frac{h}{L} \qquad (8.2)$$

where Q is the volume rate of flow (percolation) of water normally through the rock, A is the area of the rock through which flow takes place, L is the length of the flow path, and h the excess hydrostatic head acting across L.

The two quotients Q/A and h/L are sometimes known as the *percolation velocity* (v_p) and the *hydraulic gradient* (i). Equation (8.2) is only linear at constant temperature, and permeability characteristics can be more satisfactorily expressed in terms of the *permeability constant p_c* rather than by p thus:

$$v_p = \frac{p_c}{\eta}\rho i \qquad (8.3)$$

where η is the coefficient of viscosity for water varying with temperature.

The units of p are cm/sec and p_c, cm². p_c is a constant for any permeable material, independent of the properties of the percoating liquid. p can be altered by temperature in a confined range and possibly by solution of soluble minerals. Average values of p_c, p at 15°C and the apparent porosity n_a are quoted in Table 8.1.

TABLE 8.1   Permeability and Porosity of Rocks

Rock	p_c (cm²)	p (at 15°C) (cm/sec)	n_a (%)
Granite	0·001 –0·05	10^{-4}–10^{-5}	1 –4
Gabbro	0·00001–0·002	10^{-5}–10^{-7}	0·1–0·5
Micro-granite	0·001 –0·05	10^{-4}–10^{-5}	1 –3
Dolerite	0·00001–0·002	10^{-5}–10^{-7}	0·1–0·5
Basalt	0·001 –0·05	10^{-4}–10^{-5}	1 –3
Sandstone	0·2 –0·3	10^{-3}–10^{-4}	4 –20
Shale	0·02 –0·3	10^{-3}–10^{-4}	5 –20
Limestone	0·02 –0·3	10^{-3}–10^{-4}	5 –15
Quartzite	0·00001–0·002	10^{-5}–10^{-7}	0·2–0·6
Marble	0·001 –0·05	10^{-4}–10^{-5}	2 – 4
Slate	0·00001–0·05	10^{-4}–10^{-7}	0·1– 1

The values of p_c, p are important since they give an indication of the rate of water flow through a particular rock. An impermeable rock, such as a rock with a permeability constant less than 0·001, is unlikely to pass or contain a significant quantity of water, and under certain circumstances will pass only sufficient water to keep pace with evaporation. Such considerations are of great importance in the choice of dam sites and D'Arcy's law is the basis of the study of *hydrology* – the underground transport of water. In the design of structures in rock the permeability of a rock is important in so far as it indicates the ability of a rock to transport water to a structure or contain water itself in significant quantities.

8.2 Effect of Water on Rock Strength

When a rock is immersed in water, its strength is reduced. This effect has been demonstrated by Price, 1960; Handin *et al.*, 1963; and Colback and Wiid, 1965, and may be explained through analysis of a section of rock in confinement (Figure 8.1) subject to maximum and minimum

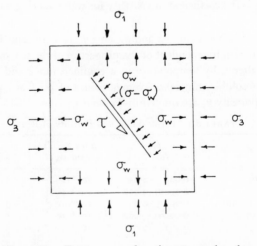

Figure 8.1   Forces on a plane in saturated rock.

principal stresses σ_1, σ_3. If the rock is saturated, with water contained in its pores, the water unable to escape and virtually incompressible will be subject to a hydraulic pressure, σ_w, equivalent to the pore-water pressure throughout the interconnected pore space.

Thus the *effective* (compressive) principal stresses in the rock will be decreased respectively to $\sigma_1 - \sigma_w$ and $\sigma_3 - \sigma_w$. By substituting in eqns (2.9) and (2.10) this gives normal and shear stresses in the plane of maximum shear (Mohr failure plane) equivalent to:

$$\sigma = \frac{(\sigma_1 - \sigma_w) + (\sigma_3 - \sigma_w)}{2} - \left[\frac{(\sigma_1 - \sigma_w) - (\sigma_3 - \sigma_w)}{2}\right] \cos 2\alpha \quad (8.4)$$

$$\tau = \left[\frac{(\sigma_1 - \sigma_w) - (\sigma_3 - \sigma_w)}{2}\right] \sin 2\alpha \quad (8.5)$$

reducing to:

$$\sigma = \frac{(\sigma_1 + \sigma_3)}{2} - \frac{(\sigma_1 - \sigma_3)}{2} \cos 2\alpha - \sigma_w \quad (8.6)$$

$$\tau = \frac{(\sigma_1 - \sigma_3)}{2} \sin 2\alpha \quad (8.7)$$

Thus as compared with the dry state (eqns 2.9 and 2.10) the shear stress τ remains unchanged on the plane of maximum shear, while the effective normal stress, σ, is decreased by an amount equal to the pore-water pressure σ_w.

Thus, under the conditions for failure as demonstrated through the Coulomb–Navier criterion of failure, the failure envelope for a saturated porous rock will be given by (Figure 8.2)

$$\tau = S_s + (\sigma - \sigma_w) \tan \phi \quad (8.8)$$

an envelope parallel to the envelope for a dry porous rock in which the constant shear intercept S_s is reduced by a constant amount equal to $\sigma_w \tan \phi$ (Figure 8.2). This theoretical analysis may be compared with

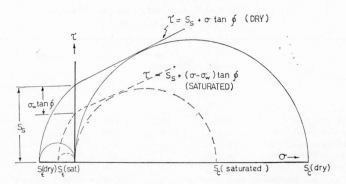

Figure 8.2   Effect of pore-water pressure on rock strength.

a practical case observed by Colback and Wiid (Figure 8.3) in sandstone where the strength was reduced by 50% on saturation.

The actual magnitude and importance of σ_w is a matter of opinion. It must depend to a certain extent on the saturation of the rock and upon its porosity and permeability; it also depends on the pressure act-

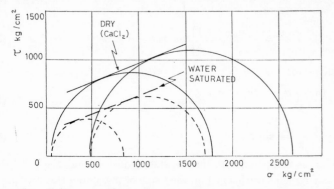

Figure 8.3   Failure envelopes for dry and saturated quartzite. (After Colback and Wiid.)

ing on the rock, i.e. its depth of burial. Obviously a rock with a high pore-water pressure but with low porosity, permeability and saturation will contain very little absorbed water and hence show few of the characteristics associated with pore-water pressure, whereas a rock with a high pore-water content might be considerably weakened at low pressures. Nevertheless the effect of pore-water content on porous rocks tends to be remarkably similar. Table 8.2 (Colback and Wiid,

TABLE 8.2   Effect of Water Content on Rock Strength
(After Colback and Wiid, Price)

Rock	Porosity n_a (%)	Air-dry Pore-water Content, a (% saturation)	Relative Strength (%)		
			Dry	Air-dry	Saturated
Quartzitic Shale	0·25	25	100	64	53
Pennant Sandstone	2·5	42	100	51	45
Markham Sandstone	6	22	100	57	
Parkgate Sandstone	10	9	100	68	45
Quartzite Sandstone	15	4	100	70	48
Darley Dale Sandstone	19·5	3	100	80	45

Price, 1960) gives the relative strengths of five sandstones and a shale under dry and saturated conditions.

An example of the effect of percentage saturation (i.e. the ratio between pore-water volume and total pore space) on uniaxial compressive strengths is given in Figure 8.4 (Colback and Wiid).

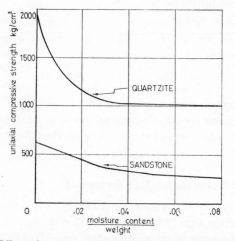

Figure 8.4 Effect of water content on rock strength. (After Colback and Wiid.)

It is difficult to arrive at a hard-and-fast relationship between percentage saturation a and uniaxial compressive strength, but as an empirical rule it could be taken that $S_c \propto 1a^2$ down to a minimum value of S_c equivalent to 45–50% of the value of S_c in a wholly dried condition. This would certainly tend to explain low values of S_c obtained during *in-situ* tests on porous rocks.

Where the porosity of the rock is less than 0·1 it is doubtful whether complete saturation will occur, in which case strength reduction will be minimal.

Apart from exceptional cases such as an aquaclude with no surface access, or a clay cut-off where free and pore-water may be contained at artesian pressures, the magnitude of σ_w in a saturated rock will depend largely on its depth of burial. Under ideally hydrostatic conditions this would be equivalent to:

$$\sigma_w = \rho h \qquad (8.9)$$

where h is the depth, and ρ is the density of the water in shallow porous rocks and of the rock in deep rocks.

However, under normal primitive stress conditions, where the vertical stress is assumed equal to ρh, the pore-pressure can be equated to the lateral confining stress, thus:

$$\sigma_w = k\rho h \qquad (8.10)$$

where k may have a value between 0·5 and 0·9 depending on depth and strata condition (see Section 9.1).

In other words, under most conditions in wet rock, the pore-water pressure can be equated to the confining pressure σ_3 in which case eqn (8.6) becomes:

$$\sigma = \frac{\sigma_1 - \sigma_3}{2} - \frac{\sigma_1 - \sigma_3}{2} \cos 2\alpha \qquad (8.11)$$

Thus if eqn (2.9) gives the normal stress in a wholly dry rock, eqn (8.11) will give the resultant effective normal stress in a saturated rock. In most rocks, the actual normal stress will lie between these two extremes.

8.3 Effect of Water on Rock Deformation

The effect of pore-water pressure on the modulus of elasticity of a rock is less clear. From eqns (3.6), (3.7) and (3.8), it can be deduced that the effect of a pore-water pressure equal to σ_w would lead to an equivalent decrease in strain of $0·5\sigma_w/E$. This in effect would indicate a decreased modulus of elasticity and experience has shown that in porous rocks in particular, saturation leads to a decrease in the modulus of elasticity. Obert *et al.* (1946) show that for porous sandstones and limestones, E is between 20% and 40% less in a saturated state than in a desiccator dried state. For slate and siltstone this is reduced to 0–5%, while in the case of granite and marble E is in fact increased in the wet state by as much as 30%. However, the moisture content is low in these latter four cases.

A fairly radical explanation for deformation anomalies in wet rock is put forward by Boozer *et al.* (1962) on the basis of the Rehbinder (Rehbinder *et al.*, 1948) effect. This postulates that all phenomena due to pore-water are caused by a reduction of free surface energy between the rock constituents, brought about by the absorption process. In other words, the cohesive structure of the rock is weakened by the presence of a liquid in the pores, and since all deformation and failure characteristics are influenced by this cohesion, they will be affected in proportion to the amount and pressure of the liquid present; strength and elastic modulus being decreased and flow potentialities increased.

There is little evidence available as to the exact effect of water on the flow properties of rocks, although De Sitter (1956) suggests that in porous rocks there is an inverse linear relationship between the coefficient of viscosity and the water content. This means that the rock tends to become less viscous with increasing water content with consequent increase in creep strain and strain rate at specified stress levels.

It is, however, difficult to obtain any accurate information on the effect of water on specific rocks, mainly because rocks where time-dependent deformation is not a significant factor in a dry state will not develop substantially different properties when wet, whereas rocks which might tend to flow in a dry state (particularly any which contain clay minerals) may develop spectacular and quite unpredictable deformation properties when subject to various degrees of saturation. For instance, mechanical disturbance of wet shales may cause them to revert to their original state. Under such conditions they will react as a typical loose clay soil and creep data based on assumed initial competence will have little value.

In rocks formerly classed as *semi-elastic*, the creep constant A, at medium stress levels, is likely to be increased by as much as an order of magnitude in a fully saturated state. This can have significant effects in some rocks, altering their mechanical reactions from primarily elastic to primarily viscous.

8.4 Effect of Water on Dynamic Properties

Biot (1956) has shown theoretically that a seismic wave propagated through a saturated porous rock attentuates more rapidly than a comparable wave in a dry rock, the energy loss mechanism being due to viscous absorption, proportional to the permeability and porosity of the medium. Biot's theory has been confirmed experimentally by Gregory (1962) and Schön (1966), who have demonstrated several important anomalies affecting the dynamic properties of porous rocks.

Most important is the fact that whilst the presence of pore-water causes a decrease in *static* elastic constants for many rocks, it results in an increase of both compressive (P) and shear (S) wave velocities and a consequent increase in the apparent values of the *dynamic* elastic constants calculated from eqns (6.8) and (6.9). A further anomaly concerns the relationship of the dynamic elastic constants to the porosity; as the porosity of a rock (assumed to be essentially porous) decreases, so the dynamic modulus of elasticity increases. This was discussed in earlier chapters. Figure 8.5 confirms the essentially curvilinear form of the relationship.

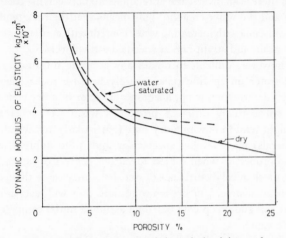

Figure 8.5 Relationship between modulus of elasticity and porosity for dry and saturated sandstone. (After Gregory.)

Since the difference in dry and wet dynamic moduli can be as much as 100% at zero pressure, and since few tests are conducted on artificially dried samples, it is evident that serious errors can and do arise in dynamic moduli testing procedures, where the degree of saturation of a sample is not stated.

9

Effect of Temperature and Pressure on Rock Properties

The effect of temperature and pressure on the mechanical behaviour of rocks has rather more relevance to the structural geologist's interpretation of tectonic movement than to the engineer's design of structures in rock, since neither mines nor engineering works are likely to be constructed under the extreme conditions of temperature and pressure required to affect rock reactions. Nevertheless a knowledge of the basic effects of temperature and pressure is important, both for completeness and for understanding of basic reactions at depth in the earth's crust.

9.1 Stress levels in the Earth's Crust

The *primitive* stresses acting in the earth's crust are influenced primarily by the weight of the overlying strata, and to a lesser extent by the presence of geological deformational structures, surface topography and residual deformation stresses (see Chapter 10). Under simple conditions – say level strata of uniform thickness – the normal assumption is that primitive stresses may be resolved into a vertical principal stress, σ_z, and two equal horizontal principal stresses σ_x, σ_y. In this case the vertical stress can be calculated simply as:

$$\sigma_z = \rho h \tag{9.1}$$

and the horizontal stress:

$$\sigma_x = k\rho h \tag{9.2}$$

where h is the depth of burial, ρ the density of the rock and k a constant depending on the physical characteristics of the strata.

If ρ is assumed equal to 2·5 gm/cm³, this gives a vertical stress equal to 250 kg/cm² per kilometre depth.

Typical assumptions to determine values of k are: (i) that the rock is completely viscous and that flow under sustained load will eventually relieve all stress differentials to produce hydrostatic stress distribution, whence $\sigma_x = \sigma_z$ and $k = 1$, (ii) that the rock is completely rigid $(E = \infty)$ requiring no lateral restraint and hence $k = 0$. Obviously these are both unrealistic except under exceptional conditions, and it is evident that since a rock is normally intermediate between the two extremes, k is likely to have an intermediate value, constant for specific conditions. There is an erroneous tendency to equate this intermediate value with purely elastic rock conditions, in which it is assumed that the lateral stress is just sufficient to prevent any lateral strain in the earth's crust. This gives:

$$\sigma_x = \frac{\sigma_z \nu}{1 - \nu}, \; k = \frac{\nu}{1 - \nu} \qquad (9.3)$$

suggesting values of $k = 0.33$ for average values of Poisson's ratio $(\nu = 0.25)$, and $k = 0.5$ for optimum values of ν (0.33). In fact, observed values of k (Leeman, 1964) vary between 0.5 and 0.9, indicating a degree of visco-elasticity at some stage of the tectonic process.

These values represent the average condition. In districts subject to unnaturally large lateral stresses (such as Sweden) horizontal stresses up to three times the vertical stress have been recorded (Hast 1958).

9.2 Strength and Elasticity

At normal pressures and temperatures and with low rates of strain most competent rocks behave in a brittle or semi-brittle manner. Three main factors can cause deviation from this state; they are:

(i) High confining pressures.
(ii) High temperatures.
(iii) High rates of strain.

Normally these factors are introduced either by tectonic movement or high levels of dynamic loading and their primary effect is to introduce a ductile or *plastic flow* zone into the rock stress/strain relationship, at the same time increasing in the case of (i) and (ii) or decreasing in the case of (iii) the yield point of the rock equivalent to the compressive or tensile strength, but perhaps more correctly defined as the ultimate strength in this case.

The effects of high confining pressures have been studied by various workers and in particular in the classical experiments of Griggs (1936). Figure 9.1 shows the effect of different confining pressures on the stress/strain relationship for marble at room temperature. This shows clearly how in an initially brittle rock, ductility can be introduced by increased confining pressure, although the levels at which plastic flow becomes significant – that is the approximate transition point between brittle and ductile failure (4,000 kg/cm²) – are outside normal static pressure levels. The increase in yield strength is particularly interesting, but this is not necessarily synonymous with an increase in the elastic limit, since much of the additional 'elastic strain' in rocks at these pressure levels must be permanent (see Figure 9.4). The effect of confinement on the modulus of elasticity only attains significance at low pressures in highly porous rocks due to compression of pore space.

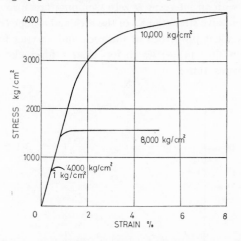

Figure 9.1   Effect of confining pressure on stress/strain relationship for marble. (After Griggs.)

The transition point between brittle and ductile behaviour is of considerable significance in considering the tectonic origin of geological deformation and failure structures and may have some bearing on the design of underground mine openings at depths in excess of 2,000–3,000 metres depending on the type of rock involved. For general rock types this may be stated in terms of confining pressure at room temperature (20 °C) (Table 9.1), although it must be remembered that even at these confining pressures, considerable differential stress may be required to induce plastic flow.

The effect of confining pressure on the yield point/ultimate strength of a rock (at room temperature) can be seen from Figure 9.2. For most sedimentary rocks (Handin and Hager, 1957, 1958) the relationship

TABLE 9.1   Brittle/Ductile Failure Limit – Confining Pressures

Rock	Pressure (kg/cm^2)	Equivalent Depth (km)
Igneous Rocks (Bridgeman, 1952)	5,000	25–30
Compact Sedimentary	2,000	10
Normal Sedimentary	1,000	4
Porous Sedimentary	100–500	0.5–2

between ultimate strength (S_u) and confining pressures (σ_c) is within limits linear, with an intercept at zero confining pressure equal to the uniaxial compressive strength (S_c) of the rock and a slope (m) related to the time-dependent properties of the rock and varying from 2–3 for rocks with low flow properties to less than 1 for rocks with highly viscous properties, thus:

$$S_u = S_c + m\sigma_c \tag{9.4}$$

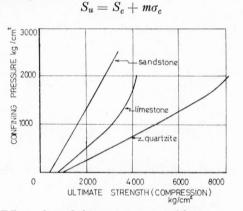

Figure 9.2   Effect of confining pressure on ultimate strength at room temperature. (After Handin and Hager.)

In stronger sedimentary rocks (there are insufficient data available for igneous rocks due to their high brittle/ductile limit) the relationship is curvilinear, approximating to:

$$S_u = S_c + \exp\left[m(\sigma_c - \sigma_L)\right] \tag{9.5}$$

where σ_L represents the limiting confining pressure for the ductile/brittle transition.

However, it is academic to discuss brittle/ductile transition in stronger sedimentary and igneous rocks purely as a confining pressure phenomenon at room temperature. This would mean that an igneous rock would still be expected to fail in shear at a depth of 20–30 km, when in fact in some parts of the earth's crust, rock at this depth would be so hot as to be approaching a molten state.

It can be shown that at most points in the earth's crust there is an average temperature (geothermal) gradient of 1 °C per 30-m rock thickness, which means that at these depths a temperature of 1,000 °C would be expected. At maximum engineering depths around 3,000 m, the rock temperature of 100 °C is unlikely to have any significant effect, but at greater magnitudes the secondary creep phenomenon of deformation at constant strain rate will affect ductility and strength to an increasing extent.

The effects of temperature rise from 24 °C to 300 °C on the stress/ strain characteristics of three rock types can be seen in Figure 9.3 (after

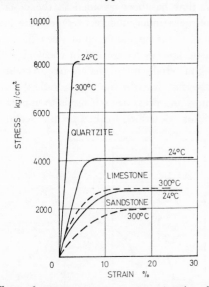

Figure 9.3 Effect of temperature on stress/strain characteristics at 2,000 kg/cm² confining pressure. (After Handin and Hager.)

Handin and Hager, 1957, 1958). Although not necessarily typical of all rock types, this demonstrates the increasing ductility and lowering yield point, characteristic of the mechanical effects of high temperature in rock. This is shown most strikingly in quartzitic igneous rocks, particularly resistant to plastic flow under high confining pressures, which nevertheless have been found to exhibit flow and failure at confining pressures of 2,000 kg/cm² at temperatures in the range 200–400 °C

(Serdengecti and Boozer, 1961); a strength reduction of up to 100%. Normally, however, a close approximation can be obtained in terms of the geothermal gradient allied to confining pressure at depth if a reduction of 10–15% in strength is assumed for each 100 °C increase in temperature and equivalent 1,000 kg/cm² increase in confining pressure, or 3,000 m increase in depth, thus

$$S_u = S_u' - \frac{0 \cdot 15h}{3,000} \qquad (9.6)$$

where S_u' is the ultimate strength at room temperature (eqns 9.4, 9.5) and h is the depth in metres.

9.3 Plastic Flow under Extreme Conditions

The term *plastic* flow has been avoided in the description of time-dependent flow of rocks under moderate temperature and pressure conditions (Chapter 4), terms such as creep or visco-elastic flow being preferred, since plastic flow as recognized in rheological theory tends to idealize a yielding material with a constant irrecoverable strain reaction to stress. This does not describe the visco-elastic deformation of rocks at low temperatures and pressures – it tends to approximate, however, the ductile conditions described in the previous section.

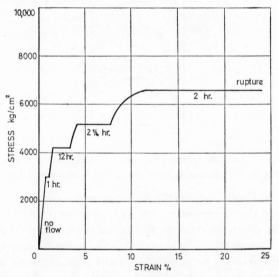

Figure 9.4   Flow of limestone at confining pressure of 10,000 kg/cm².
(After Griggs.)

The difference in action can best be explained by reference to Griggs' (1936) experiments, which demonstrate typical plastic flow in a limestone under 10,000 atmospheres confining pressure (Figure 9.4), demonstrating a constant time-dependent plastic strain with increasing strain rate at each period of constant stress, finally rupturing under sufficient stress. In the first three stages, part of the strain is recoverable and there is a limit short of rupture on the strain level. In the final stage the strain is irrecoverable and proceeds to failure. This is plastic flow – representing the secondary (and tertiary) stage of the creep curve (Chapter 4) and only visible in rock under extremes of load or temperature.

The effect of temperature on the flow process can be obtained through the Arrhenius equation, viz.:

$$\varepsilon \propto t \exp\left(-\frac{1}{T}\right), \quad \frac{d\varepsilon}{dt} \propto \exp\left(-\frac{1}{T}\right) \qquad (9.7)$$

and of stress

$$\varepsilon \propto t\sigma^2, \quad \frac{d\varepsilon}{dt} \propto \sigma^2 \qquad (9.8)$$

It is therefore evident that apart from pressure and temperature, the degree of plastic flow is also affected by the strain rate. This has been demonstrated by Heard (1963), who plotted the effect of strain rate on marble at constant temperature of 500°C and pressure of 5,000 kg/cm² (Figure 9.5). It is immediately evident that under rapid rates of loading,

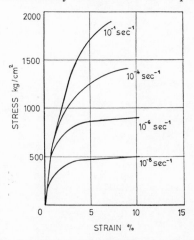

Figure 9.5 Effect of strain rate on stress/strain relationships in marble at 5,000 kg/cm² confining pressure and 500°C temperature. (After Heard.)

strength is increased and there is a tendency away from ductility and towards brittle failure. Thus strength increases with high rates of strain and, as suggested earlier, dynamic strength levels (even under unconfined loading conditions) may be considerably in excess of static strength levels.

The mechanism of plastic deformation in rocks appears to be radically different from the creep mechanism at lower pressures, which consists predominantly of intergranular slip with some slight structural adjustment. Plastic flow, on the other hand, appears to involve large-scale alteration and dislocation in the molecular bonding and crystal structure, involving primarily twinning, and basal gliding which can be identified to a greater or lesser extent in many tectonically deformed rocks.

10

Structural Features of Massive Rock

A difficulty in the consideration of rock as a structural material lies in the discontinuity of rock in its natural massive state. Just as a rock specimen may be considered a cohesive aggregate of discrete mineral particles, so a rock mass may often be considered an aggregate of separate rock particles, whose relative cohesion depends on the intensity and frequency of foliation and jointing in the rock mass.

This is an essential concept in the treatment of rock as a structural material, for to a large extent the engineering properties of rocks are governed by their behaviour in bulk as a rock mass rather than by their 'small-scale' mechanical reactions, although in fact the difference may be minimal. The purpose of this chapter is therefore to estimate the effect of specific geological structures on massive rock properties, particularly as they might affect the design of structures in massive rock.

Basically there are three main types of structural feature affecting rock masses: foliation surfaces (including all parallel rock surfaces from bedding planes to schistosity), folds, and joints and faults. The first and the last of these features are particularly important since they represent potential planes of weakness in the rock mass inclined at various angles to the vertical and/or the direction of major principal stress through the agency of various tectonic movements – primarily folding in sedimentary rock, as evidenced in the second type of structural feature. Thus, definition of a rock mass for the purposes of engineering design must include information on foliation and joint direction, spacing and inclination, and the position and inclination of any faults.

10.1 Deformation and Failure Structures in the Earth's Crust

The simplest types of structural feature, found in most rock masses, are *foliation* surfaces, the term used to describe parallel surfaces making up a layered or banded rock structure. This general term can be used to describe *stratification* or primary layering in sedimentary rocks, subdivided into *bedding* (layer spacing greater than 1 cm), *lamination* (layer spacing between 1 cm and 1 mm) and *lamellation* (layer spacing less than 1 mm) and secondary layering in metamorphic rocks (*schistosity*) resulting from the reorientation of platy minerals such as mica (Wallis *et al.*, 1967).

In addition to these features, foliation is also exhibited as *cleavage*, primarily a property of mineral crystals and metamorphic rocks (slate), apparent in the ability of a rock to split along an indefinite number of closely spaced parallel surfaces (*true* cleavage) or a limited number of predetermined surfaces (*false* cleavage). False cleavage should not be confused with true cleavage and is normally an example of close faulting, folding or jointing.

All foliation may be qualified by the ease with which it is distinguished and its shape, but in rock engineering problems its primary importance is as a single plane or series of planes of weakness in a rock mass. Normally foliation surfaces represent a considerably stronger form of weakness plane than a joint or fault, and in many cases there is little difference between the properties of rocks at right angles to and paralle to the direction of minor foliation. A useful guide is suggested by Donath (1964), who shows an ultimate strength reduction of approximately 50% in slate when the direction of cleavage is parallel to the direction of maximum shear. However, in sandstone, shale, and gneiss, where the foliation is less pronounced, Youash (1966) shows that the ultimate strength reduction can be as low as 5% – a figure which can be conveniently ignored. Thus, unless foliation (or anisotropy) is pronounced, it may be ignored. Cleavage and major bedding planes are considered in the following sections.

Folds, normally found in stratified rock, retain the primary form of the rock structure, while having been subjected to deformation in all directions, although, due to the predominance of tangential forces in the earth's crust, major deformation is in the vertical plane, giving rise to the popular representation of a fold with an upfold or *anticline* structure and a downfold or *syncline* structure.

The actual formation of the fold depends on three major factors: the competence or incompetence of the rock, the magnitudes of temperature and stresses to which it is subjected and the direction of the stress. These factors together give rise to two parallel classifications of folds, based on genesis and geometry. In the former, folds are classified as: (i) flow folds, (ii) flexural slip folds and (iii) shear folds – in the latter as: (*a*) disharmonic, (*b*) concentric and (*c*) similar folds. Simple representation of the geometric classification is shown in Figure 10.1. The genetic classification is the least simple; *flow* folds are formed under high temperature and pressure conditions and are normally either *disharmonic* or *similar* in shape. *Flexural slip* folds, however, are always *concentric*, and *shear* folds are always *similar* in shape.

Because they are formed largely under conditions of plastic flow, *flow* folds when similar in shape tend to show a high degree of preferred orientation and a high order of symmetry. On the other hand, flow folds which are disharmonic in shape (ptygmatic folds) exhibit little specific orientation or symmetry in any direction.

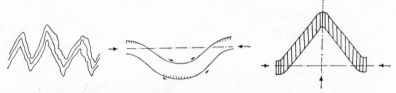

(a) DISHARMONIC (flow) FOLD   (b) CONCENTRIC (flexural slip) FOLD   (c) SIMILAR (flow or shear) FOLD

Figure 10.1   Types of folding.

Flexural slip and *shear* folds, although formed under high-stress conditions, exhibit considerably less plastic deformation, being formed mainly by shear and tensile failure under semi-brittle deformation conditions. In *flexural slip* folds all movement due to failure is parallel to the bedding, and the bedding retains its original thickness. The folding therefore follows a pattern of elastic deformation (Figure 10.1b), failure planes occurring parallel to the bed and tension cracks and sometimes 'hinge faults' at right angles to the bed on the sides subject to tension. This type of folding occurs primarily in the upper parts of the earth's crust and the deforming stresses exerted are mainly horizontal.

Shear folding on the other hand is probably caused by a subhorizontal major principal stress and a lateral or vertical constraining stress (this can also be true for *similar* shaped flow folds). Conditions of deformation are much nearer to the plastic state than in flexural slip folding, and all movement is parallel to shear surfaces (Figure 10.1c), irrespective of the bed orientation. These shear surfaces, absent in similar shaped flow folds, are a feature of the shear failure process, in the course of which the bed is deformed to consistent vertical but uneven normal thickness. The shear surfaces are an example of *cleavage*, sometimes *false* cleavage, particularly in metamorphic similar fold domains, where the surfaces are defined by closely spaced folds or hinge faults, and sometimes true cleavage – usually in low-grade metamorphic terrain.

Flexural slip and shear folds or combinations of the two are the most common type of folding. Mechanically they are similar and folds of intermediate depth will combine the essential features of both. The occurrence of cleavage in association with shear folding is, however, often an indication of initial weakness or incompetence in the folded rock. For instance, true cleavage is exhibited most noticeably in deformed shales, whereas flexural slip folding is an indication of strength or competence and is normally associated with sandstones and other

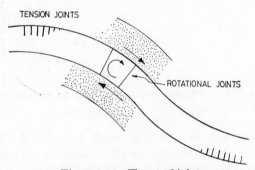

TENSION JOINTS

ROTATIONAL JOINTS

Figure 10.2 Types of joint.

massive rocks. This is important, for the type of folding is often an indication of the condition of the original rock and the stress field surrounding it, from which it is possible to estimate the strength of the folded rock and any abnormal distribution of the post-folding primitive stresses within it. For instance, the vertical stress inside the arched peak of an anticline in competent rock would tend to be less than in unfolded rock, whereas the converse would be true in the case of a syncline.

In shear folding of incompetent rock, the planes of weakness are marked by cleavage surfaces. At the same time *joints* are formed in the competent rocks by flexural slip folding. These joints represent a complete fracture in the rock as distinct from cleavage, which may appear as an internal structural weakness in the rock. Apart from pre-existing joints due to shrinkage, which may be irregular, joint formations in sedimentary rocks are invariably regular. The most common type of joints are *tension* joints at right angles to the bedding plane (Figure 10.2).

These are developed in the region of maximum curvature on the fold and are caused by tensile fracture of the rock. Rotational joints also occur at right angles to the bedding plane and are formed by interaction between the beds during folding, which generates rotational stresses within the bed. Jointing parallel to the bed also occurs in exceptional circumstances when vertical compression forces open shear-fracture planes formed during folding. These are known as *shear* joints.

Joints also occur in cooling magma. These may appear as shrinkage joints in granites and are notable as sources of mineralization.

Since joints mark a specific fracture or plane of weakness in a rock, they have considerable importance where rock is considered as a

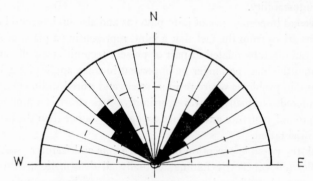

Figure 10.3   Strike frequency diagram.

structural material – more so than faults since they occur more commonly and are less obvious. They are particularly important in that the presence of joints may reduce the apparent strength of a rock mass as compared with strength tests conducted on a small scale, particularly if the joint orientation is close to the direction of shear failure. For this reason it is desirable to know the joint pattern in a district where engineering work is imminent.

The joint pattern is normally represented on a *strike frequency* diagram, which records for a given area or location the number of joints observed and their direction of strike. These are then plotted on a semicircular net, divided into 10° segments, representing the direction of strike, and the number of joints occurring parallel to the strike direction in each segment are plotted (Figure 10.3). Depending on the relative magnitude of the joints (major or minor) and the type of joint (tension or shear), a series of diagrams can be obtained for a particular location. Unless this represents a particularly complex situation the diagram will show groups of joints at fixed orientations, representing the preferred joint direction in a particular area. If the geological survey is extended by taking random samples over a wider area there should be some correlation between the strike frequency diagram built up for each sampling point in the area.

The prime importance in establishing a joint pattern for an area rests in the location of likely planes of weakness – both surface and underground – for a joint, or an induced crack pattern can be equally well determined in a series of underground excavations. Once the planes of weakness have been established, an excavation or structure can be planned to derive maximum benefit from the direction representing optimum stability.

A second important use of joint patterns and also underground crack patterns arises from the fact that a joint, representing a plane of stress relief, can often be related to past or present tectonic stress directions. Although this may no longer be important in some applications, it can be of use in problems where residual stress and stored strain energy are encountered. Normally, however, primitive rock stress is a property of underground structure and surface topography rather than the original stress orientation.

With the possible exception of tension joints and features associated with flexural/concentric folding, virtually all deformation, distortion and fracture in rock under compression is caused by movement along shear planes. This has been amply demonstrated in previous chapters and sections. *Faults* are no exception and can be defined simply as large-scale movement along an extended shear plane. In other words they are an extension of the process of shear and flow folding on a concentrated scale.

There are three main types of faulting (Anderson, 1951): normal faults, reverse faults and wrench faults. They are formed by the same shearing process and differ only in the varying directions of the principal stresses causing fracture.

Normal faults (Figure 10.4a) are formed when the major principal stress (σ_1) acts in a near-vertical direction and the intermediate and minor principal stresses in near-horizontal directions. The resulting fracture takes the form of a shear slip at an angle of slip(α) to the vertical, approximating to the Mohr angle of failure for the type of rock.

The conditions for formation of normal faults tend to occur in the upper part of the earth's crust, where although σ_1 may not be large, the minor stress σ_3 could under certain circumstances be represented by a lateral tension stress of opposite (negative) sign. There is therefore some similarity in origin between the normal fault and a cleavage surface in shear folding. The same process could also occur in flexural/concentric folding if tension joints were exacerbated by vertical stress concentrations.

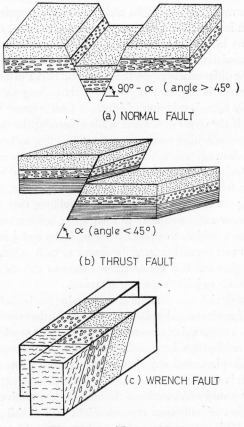

$90° - \alpha$ (angle > 45°)

(a) NORMAL FAULT

α (angle < 45°)

(b) THRUST FAULT

(c) WRENCH FAULT

Figure 10.4 **Types** of fault.

If, under similar conditions, the lateral stress were compressive and the vertical stress were small (the conditions for folding) then fracture would cause the formation of a *reverse* fault. Thus the reverse fault represents a rapid overfold and may be compared with various fold mechanisms.

Wrench faults are formed when both major and minor principal stresses are in the horizontal plane, creating an extension in the horizontal plane instead of in the vertical plane. Such an arrangement of forces will tend to occur at depth rather than near the surface, although at greater depths there will be increased tendency towards distortion, rather than fracture.

Granted the similarity in the mechanism of folding and faulting, why are faults formed instead of folds, and vice-versa? Excepting the normal fault, which has more in common with joint formation, the directions of the forces involved are similar and the two phenomena normally occur in association. The simple explanation seems to be that it is a matter of the difference between the major and minor principal stresses. If the difference is sufficient to promote failure along a shear plane, as suggested by Mohr's criterion of failure, a fault fracture will occur on that plane. If the stress difference, while exceeding the failure limit, is insufficient – suggesting confined pressure – folding will occur.

It can be shown (De Sitter, 1957) that there is in many cases a marked geometrical relationship between jointing and faulting and between jointing and the tectonic stress directions in folding. Thus, since jointing and faulting are caused as a by-product of folding, they would be expected to show some similarity in their strike orientation, and over a particular area subject to similar stresses, faults and joints would be expected to run parallel or at right angles to each other. Fault strike frequency diagrams and combination diagrams can be obtained by similar methods to joint frequency diagrams.

The main significance of faults in engineering lies in their extent both as a plane of weakness and a possible source of further movement and in their effect on the physical features of the surrounding rocks. Major contemporary earthquakes have mainly been due to movement along an existing fault plane and any sign or knowledge of recent movement along a fault is a strong disincentive to construction or excavation. The same factor would affect works in the vicinity of a passive fault, where the imposition of additional stresses might lead to failure along the fault plane. This represents an additional hazard in the case of a thrust or wrench fault, where the nature of the stresses involved in the fault formation can lead to fracturing and weakening of large areas of the surrounding rock.

A further effect of faulting – applying on a lesser scale to major joints – is that by its existence as a plane of weakness it can act as a focus for stress relief or concentration when in the vicinity of an underground excavation. Knowledge of fault locations is therefore particularly important in underground work. Their extent can also lead to water problems since they can act as a channel conveying water through relatively impervious strata.

10.2 Classification of Rock Structures

Except in the case of surface works or underground works in the vicinity of pre-existing excavations, information on failure structures must be obtained from examination of exploratory drill cores. This can often lead to difficulties in classification and identification of the various surfaces revealed, particularly in less competent rocks, where the drilling process and adjacent engineering work may induce considerable fracturing in the core.

Major structures of geological origin such as faults or main joints can normally be recognized either by displacement, or by alteration and the presence of alteration products on the structural surfaces. Bedding planes can normally be detected by depositional features on the plane. Minor structures such as laminations can often only be detected after careful laboratory examination. However, although important, the specific geological identification of all structures is often not critical in classification of rock for engineering purposes.

Previously rocks have been defined solely in terms of their mechanical properties – elasticity, rheology and strength. Definition of competence in this case is simple: a brittle elastic rock of high strength is competent, a non-elastic rock of low strength is incompetent; the relative mechanical reaction of the rock depending solely on the magnitude of the stress level to which it is subjected. At high stresses (deep excavations) this is the most important guide to rock reaction, and deformation and failure structures are important only in so far as they affect mechanical properties. However, at low stress levels, (shallow excavations) the massive state of the rock may have a critical effect. For instance, even though a rock may be by definition non-elastic and of low strength, provided its state is massive and it contains few failure structures its reaction under *low* stress conditions may be entirely satisfactory and no support for excavations may be required. Chalk and the evaporite minerals are examples of this.

On the other hand, a rock which is by definition brittle, elastic and strong, but which is heavily fissured with numerous foliation surfaces, may at stresses insufficiently high to induce competence, be completely incapable of supporting an excavation.

Similarly, the relative separation of foliation surfaces may be sufficient for competence in a narrow excavation, but may render the rock incompetent in a wider excavation. Thus any classification of rock structure must include information initially on the general massive state of the rock and then on the degree of separation of major joint/foliation surfaces in the rock.

TABLE 10.1   Structural Classification of Rock

(1) Massive state	(a)	Continuous
	(b)	Foliated
(2) Joint foliation separation	(i)	Narrow (10 cm)
	(ii)	Medium (10 cm–1 m)
	(iii)	Wide (1 m–10 m)

A suggested classification is given in Table 10.1. Of major significance under low stresses, its usefulness will decrease as the stress on the excavation increases. At high stresses and in continuous rock, greater emphasis must be placed on the individual characteristics of major discontinuities and upon the effect of weakness planes on the general mechanical properties of rocks.

10.3 Effect of Failure Structures on Rock Strength

A failure or depositional structure in a rock mass becomes important when it represents a plane of weakness in the rock, indicating a preferred direction of failure.

It is possible by a simple analysis based on the Coulomb–Navier/ Mohr criteria of failure, to examine the conditions under which failure will take place along a particular plane of weakness. Basically they will be fulfilled when a weakness plane with a lower shear strength and lower coefficient of friction than the rock, appears parallel to the plane of maximum shear (Figure 10.5). In such a case, failure in the solid rock will never be possible before failure in the plane of weakness.

The actual mechanism of failure along a plane of weakness is slightly different to that of normal shear failure and may often be represented as sliding friction between two rock surfaces so that $\tau_s = \mu_s \sigma_s$, τ_s and σ_s representing the shear and normal stresses across the surface, and μ_s the coefficient of sliding friction. However, there will be some initial resistance to shear (S_R) due to roughness of the rock contact or joint infill, corresponding to the cohesion or shear strength of the rock.

Quantitative values for the shear resistance and friction coefficient of a weakness plane are difficult to determine with accuracy, even when core samples are available from exploratory drilling, due to damage incurred in the drilling process and the probable non-representative nature of the small surface areas available. Various shear tests can be devised, but they invariably give unsatisfactory results. Any generalization is equally difficult, but Jaeger (1959, 1962) suggests that for most rocks the shear resistance will be equal to between one half and one third the shear strength of the rock and that the coefficient of sliding

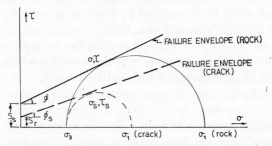

Figure 10.5   Effect of plane of weakness in the plane of maximum shear.

friction will be equal to rather more than half the coefficient of internal friction for the same rock; thus

$$S_R \simeq \frac{S_s}{3}, \quad \mu_s \simeq \frac{\mu}{2} \tag{10.1}$$

and
$$\tau_s = S_R + \mu_s \sigma_s = S_R + \sigma_s \tan \phi_s \tag{10.2}$$

another representation of the Coulomb–Navier criterion of failure.

The likelihood of failure along the plane of weakness will of course be affected by the relative inclination of the plane to the direction of the major principal stress. If this angle is taken as β, then the stresses on the plane (Figure 10.5) are given by (eqns 2.9 and 2.10):

$$\sigma_s = \frac{\sigma_1 + \sigma_3}{2} - \frac{\sigma_1 - \sigma_3}{2} \cos 2\beta \tag{10.3}$$

$$\tau_s = \frac{\sigma_1 - \sigma_3}{2} \sin 2\beta \tag{10.4}$$

If these values are substituted in eqn (10.2), a criterion of failure can be obtained in terms of the friction angle, the shear resistance and the principal stresses.

Thus if $\beta = 45°$, $\sigma_s = \sigma(\text{MAX})$ and $\tau_s = \tau(\text{MAX})$ and failure will occur along the plane, whereas if $\beta = 90°$, $0°$, $\sigma_s = \sigma_3$ and $\tau_s = 0$, and no failure will occur. Between these extremes a limiting value of β will be determined by the stress levels and plane characteristics, above which failure will not occur on the plane of weakness. For a normal joint weakness plane this will occur at between $45°$ and $65°$ to the major principal stress (Lane and Heck, 1964) conventionally taken to act in a vertical direction.

A similar analysis may be applied to specifically *anisotropic* rocks. Anisotropy in rocks is difficult to define and is consequently largely ignored, but there is no doubt that under certain conditions a distinct directional effect is encountered in stress measurements, usually in association with a laminated rock. Often, however, microscopic anisotropy is associated with megascopic bedding (weakness planes) and provided core directions are noted in testing procedures, laboratory test errors will be small compared with bed-joint effects.

In a markedly anisotropic rock, with a distinctive laminated structure, there will be a tendency to shear in the direction of the anisotropy and a corresponding tendency to resist failure in a direction normal to the anisotropy. There will therefore be an apparent weakness in the rock when the inclination of the anisotropy to the direction of major principal stress (say β) coincides with the direction of maximum shear stress ($\beta \approx 45°$).

10.4 Influence of Scale on Rock Properties

If it is accepted that with changing scale, the mechanical properties of a rock mass will change also (the degree of change being dependent primarily upon the degree to which the relative state of a rock in a large mass differs from its state in a small mass), it is a logical process to attempt to relate the small- and large-scale properties of rocks. This is particularly important in practice, for accurate testing techniques for determining the mechanical properties of rocks are limited to small rock specimens, and for true simulation the properties of the small test specimen must be repeated throughout the whole rock mass.

Igneous rocks usually approach most closely a wholly massive state, particularly near the centre of a plutonic mass, although they normally contain widely spaced tension joints. Sedimentary rocks, on the other hand, show a distinctive bedded structure, foliation surfaces bounding zones of different internal property and composition. Generally sandstone, limestones and mudstones have a more massive structure than shales, although limestones particularly in inclined strata have a tendency towards solution cavities. The additional presence of joints at right angles to the beds and to each other can lead in extreme cases to a view of the strata as a non-cohesive discontinuous aggregate of particles – normally regular and bounded by various structural features – with gaps filled with gas, water or weathering products.

Design involving individual treatment of each separate weakness plane in such a mass is obviously impracticable, and models based on soil, elastic or visco-elastic analogies are obviously limited by lack of knowledge of the general reactions of the rock mass.

An attempt to remedy this situation is the empirical approach of Protodyakonov (1964), based on a comparison of massive properties and small-scale properties of various rocks. Its usefulness is limited by the inaccuracy of large-scale testing techniques, but he suggests that the uniaxial strength of a rock in tension or compression can be related to the dimension of the test sample (L) and the spacing between major discontinuities such as joints or beds in the rock (b), viz.:

$$\frac{S}{S_M} = 1 + \frac{b(m-1)}{b+L} \qquad (10.5)$$

where S is the tensile or compressive strength of a rock from a standard test,

S_M is the equivalent strength of the massive rock,

and m is a constant known as the *mass fracture coefficient* and having values between 1 and 2 for igneous rocks, 1–3 for competent sedimentary rocks and 3–10 for incompetent sedimentary rocks in compression. Values of m for tensile tests are approximately double.

Both L and b are in centimetres, and since $L = 2 \cdot 5$ cm in the standard test, the equation may be written:

$$\frac{S}{S_M} = \frac{1+m}{1 + 2 \cdot 5/b} + 1 \qquad (10.6)$$

The magnitude of b can be related to the strength of the rock in many cases. In a soft rock – for instance, coal or shale – it may be measured in millimetres; in some competent rocks it may be as much as 10 metres. In such a case the previous relationship is of little significance and it is therefore a useful approximation to write:

$$S_M = \frac{S}{m} \qquad (10.7$$

where m lies between 1 and 2.

The difference in many cases is no more than would be expected from the presence of water in a competent porous rock. It is also important to remember that in many cases where rock acts as a structural material, the concept of massive rock is not tenable. In such a case all weakness planes affecting a rock must be treated individually.

An alternative empirical approach to size effects is the Weibull theory (Weibull, 1939) which states:

$$m \log \frac{S}{S_M} = \log \frac{V_M}{V} \tag{10.8}$$

where $\dfrac{V_M}{V}$ is the volume ratio between the rock mass and the test sample,

and m is a constant with values for rocks in the region of 10.

Whilst generally accepted as a satisfactory approach to size variations on a laboratory test scale, the Weibull theory has only limited application to massive rock.

11

Reinforcement of Massive Rock

The purpose of the present study of rock properties has been the introduction of information and criteria which may be utilized in the design of a stable structure in massive rock, necessarily involving, in the weaker rocks, techniques of stress relief and support. These techniques are to a large extent beyond the scope of the present volume, but closely related techniques by which the actual properties of rock, particularly massive rock, may be improved are, however, an important part of any study of rock properties.

It is accepted that an important aspect of the manufacture of conventional structural materials relates to the refinement or reinforcement of the material to a specified mechanical state, sufficient to meet design requirements within the structure. In rock, design requirements must normally be subjugated to the *in-situ* mechanical properties of the rock, except where these can be physically altered.

Obviously, the scope for such alteration is limited. It must be confined to the basic agencies outlined in Chapters 8–10, which may be identified as specifically affecting rock properties – namely the *water content, pressure* and *temperature*, and *massive features* of the rock.

Of these, temperature effects may be ignored since they are unlikely to affect significantly any engineering works in rock under normal or foreseeable conditions. However, the effects of pressure, water content and the presence of massive structural features may be ameliorated by the utilization of well-known techniques involving stress relief, grouting and bolting.

11.1 Flow Reduction by Stress Relief

Stress relief techniques are not strictly speaking a means of altering rock properties. Where they obtain particular importance in any cohesive material is in the reduction of the magnitude of isolated stresses surrounding a structure in the material (rock) to a value below the ultimate failure stress in the case of a brittle, quasi-elastic rock or below the stress at which the rock shows time-dependent strain (creep) characteristics in the case of a semi- or non-elastic rock.

All materials possessing cohesion (shear resistance, shear strength) in an unconfined state have a stress limit above which flow becomes a significant factor. Termed the *ductility* limit in Chapter 9, this can range from a stress of 50 kg/cm² in a saturated weak shale at room temperatures to tectonic stresses in the region of 5,000 kg/cm² at similar temperatures in strong igneous rocks.

The ductility limit may be approached quantitatively on the basis of the analysis in Chapter 4, relating the creep constant (A) to the measured elastic properties of the rock and in particular the modulus of elasticity at zero stress E_i. Thus eqn (4.19) postulates that:

$$A = \left(\frac{\sigma}{E_i}\right)^n \qquad (11.1)$$

where n is a stress-related exponent (Figure 4.5) having a near-linear relationship to the stress differential in the range:

$$1 \cdot 5 < n < 2, \quad 100 < (\sigma_1 - \sigma_3) < 1{,}500 \text{ kg/cm}^2.$$

It is therefore possible to relate A to the stress differential for the general case of a rock in compression (Figure 11.1) for various assumed values of E_i (Table 3.1). If an arbitrary value of A is then selected as representing the limits beyond which time-dependent deformation will become insupportable (say $A = 10^{-5}$, Table 4.6), this can serve as an

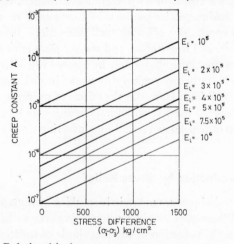

Figure 11.1 Relationship between creep constant and stress difference.

indicator of the maximum stress difference to which any structure in competent rock with an assumed E_i value may be subjected.

If during design or construction it is evident that this value will be exceeded, it is then that techniques of stress relief and reduction may be utilized to preserve the rigidity of the rock in the structure. These can take various forms depending on the life and risk acceptance of the structure.

The simplest remedy, since time-dependent strain is a property (in a stress situation other than uniaxial) of the principal stress difference, consists of the preloading of the excavation sides with some form of hydraulic or other support device, thus reducing the differential stresses induced by the excavation. However, since total preloading over the whole excavation would obviously be uneconomical, such methods generally reduce to partial support systems, a temporary remedy only, in ground subject to severe creep.

Where permanent stress reduction is required it may be necessary to provide an alternative stress focus near to the excavation, creating a zone of stress relief in the actual vicinity of the excavation. Kvapil (1963) discusses various methods of achieving this through the use of pre-stressed inclusions or dummy excavations.

11.2 Rockbolt Reinforcement

Structural reinforced concrete may be strengthened by casting it around rods or bars under tension, so that when the concrete sets, adhesion between the concrete and the tensioned reinforcing rods will place the concrete into a state of precompression. In this state, it will display increased resistance to failure when subjected to shear or tensile stresses in the direction of reinforcement.

This common form of reinforcement has a direct analogy in the use of rockbolts as a means of reinforcement in rock, except that in the case of a rockbolt, the precompression is applied to the solid rock surrounding the completed structure, through tensioning of an anchored bolt, rather than by adhesion to a preset tensioned rod. Thus, whereas in a pre-stressed concrete member (or an unstressed reinforced member) the critical strengthening factor is the bonding between the rods and the concrete, in precompressed rock, the critical factor is the strength of the anchorage. A rock which is to be strengthened by bolting, must therefore be sufficiently strong and continuous on a limited scale to provide a firm anchorage for the bolts, although under most conditions,

K

anchorages may be provided by cement grouting. The bolts must also have adequate length to create a precompression zone of sufficient extent around a structure to resist failure stresses.

The degree of precompression available from the use of rockbolts depends on the diameter and strength of the bolt, the strength and deformation properties of the anchorage rock and the density of bolting. Of these, the second is critical in the determination of the other two.

The type of rock where strengthening by precompression will be needed, will be either strong and subject to macrofracture and well-defined weakness planes, or weak and strongly foliated. In the former case, an anchorage in the rock will be subject only to the possible brittle failure at the end of the bolt, and provided the pressure exerted through the bolt does not exceed the compressive strength of the rock, failure will be avoided.

The maximum load (W) per bolt will then be given by $W = S_c.a$, where a is the cross-sectional area of the anchorage and S_c is the compressive strength of the rock, and the precompression σ_p applied to the rock by:

$$\sigma_p = \frac{nW}{A} \qquad (11.2)$$

where n is the number of bolts, and A the total area of bolted rock (assuming even distribution).

The effect of this precompression on rock properties will depend on its relationship to the principal stresses acting on the rock. Since it is unidirectional, its effect will depend primarily on its orientation with respect to the major principal stress. Three cases (Figure 11.2) may be considered in relation to possible applications: where the direction of precompression is (a) parallel to the minor principal stress, (b) parallel to the major principal stress and (c) normal to the plane of maximum shear.

The solutions may be obtained by substitution in eqns (2.9) and (2.10), in the manner of eqns (8.4) to (8.10), a similar case where pore-water pressure was considered. Thus, in the first case the effect of precompression stress will be to increase the minor principal stress by an amount σ_p, giving normal and shear stresses on the plane of maximum shear:

$$\sigma_a = \sigma + \frac{\sigma_p}{2}(1 - \cos 2\alpha) \qquad (11.3)$$

$$\tau_a = \tau - \frac{\sigma_p}{2}\sin 2\alpha \qquad (11.4)$$

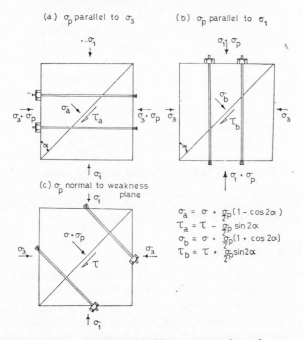

$$\sigma_a = \sigma + \frac{\sigma_p}{2}(1 - \cos 2\alpha)$$
$$\tau_a = \tau - \frac{\sigma_p}{2}\sin 2\alpha$$
$$\sigma_b = \sigma + \frac{\sigma_p}{2}(1 + \cos 2\alpha)$$
$$\tau_b = \tau + \frac{\sigma_p}{2}\sin 2\alpha$$

Figure 11.2   Effect of bolting on stress in a plane.

and a Coulomb–Navier failure envelope (assuming $\alpha = 45°$) equal to:

$$\tau = S_s + \frac{\sigma_p}{2}(1 + \tan \phi) + \sigma \tan \phi \qquad (11.5)$$

Similarly the second case will give a failure envelope:

$$\tau = S_s - \frac{\sigma_p}{2}(1 - \tan \phi) + \sigma \tan \phi \qquad (11.6)$$

and the third case:

$$\tau = S_s + \sigma_p \tan \phi + \sigma \tan \phi \qquad (11.7)$$

For average values of ϕ (Figure 11.3) these will represent a weakening of the structure in the second case and a strengthening in the other two cases, maximum strengthening occurring when the rockbolt precompression bolsters the minor principal or confining stress.

In the case of a specific weakness plane, the analysis of eqns (10.1) to (10.4) may be used. In the simplest case where the rockbolt load acts directly across the surface, conditions for failure will be given by:

$$\tau_s = S_R + (\sigma_s + \sigma_p) \tan \phi_s \qquad (11.8)$$

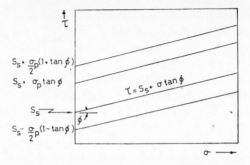

Figure 11.3   Effect of bolting on shear strength.

In other cases, the value of σ_p will be determined by the angle between the plane and the major principal stress.

11.3 Rock Stabilization by Grouting

The term grouting is used to describe the injection of cement suspensions under pressure into voids or cracks in massive rock. The primary requirements of a grout are (i) that it be sufficiently fine and viscous to penetrate the finest capillary openings in the rock and (ii) that following placement it solidifies or gels sufficiently to fill all voids and fissures with a solid material, thus both increasing the strength of the rock and preventing influx of water.

The most widely used grouting material in rock treatment is Portland cement with additives designed to improve its viscosity and act as filling material, while at the same time retaining a high setting strength (Table 11.1). Common additives are montmorillonite clays (bentonites)

TABLE 11.1   Typical Grout Strengths (after du Bois, 1963)

Grout Type (%)	28-day Compressive Strength (kg/cm²)
Portland Cement (100)	620
,, ,, (25) + Flyash	530
,, ,, (50) + ,,	660
,, ,, (75) + ,,	780
,, ,, (25) + Quartzite filler	100
,, ,, (50) + ,, ,,	420
,, ,, (75) + ,, ,,	560
(All + 2% bentonite)	

and sodium silicate to improve viscosity, and flyash or fine sand as an inert filling material. Addition of either in large quantities can weaken the strength of the grout, except in the case of fillers such as flyash which may have inherent binding properties, although bentonite suspensions and sodium silicate mixtures with their intrinsic ability to gel on settlement can be used where an extremely fine and free-flowing grout is required for the primary purpose of reducing the permeability of a porous rock.

The pressure at which grout may be pumped into rock strata depends on the degree of confinement, the strength of the rock and the presence of large-scale discontinuities, factors which may combine to cause failure in the rock when subject to the hydraulic pressures associated with grouting. With this reservation, the higher the pressure the more effective will be the penetration, spread and strength of the grout. In places where rock is particularly weak, containing numerous voids, high grouting pressures which might initially fracture the rock can be obtained through repeat injections after voids have been filled and the rock stabilized by low-pressure injections of coarse grout.

Grouting can therefore be used to improve rock properties in two ways: through the reduction of water content by increased permeability and reduced porosity of a rock, and through consolidation of weak and fractured rock masses by bonding of cracks and weakness planes.

Quantitative data on the actual effects of grout on rock properties are rare, since post-grouting observations are largely qualitative, quantitative research being confined to the flow properties of the grout.

Results obtained by Little et al. (1963) in weak sandstones suggest that permeability may be reduced by a maximum of 50% under good conditions. Effects on strength are confined to the macro-scale and under good conditions the strength of highly fractured rock should be raised to the level of the strengths associated with the grout (Table 11.1).

12

Measurement of Stress and Strain in Massive Rock

Previous chapters have been concerned solely with a statement of the fundamental properties of rock, as distinct from an application of a knowledge of these properties to problems of engineering design. There is, however, a particular application of these fundamental properties which must be considered in advance of any foray into engineering design in rock, namely the measurement of stress and strain in rock, an exercise as germane to the mechanics of the design process in rock as a knowledge of the rock properties themselves. The reasons for this have been developed briefly in the previous chapters. Basically they reflect the uncertainties inherent in any statement of rock properties, whether this be due to philosophical weaknesses in the application of analytical procedures to granular materials, unsatisfactory measurement techniques or irregularities in the macroscopic structure of *in-situ* rock. These are polarized in the need for a method of measuring stresses in the vicinity of an excavation during construction as a cross-check on the efficiency of the design.

The major requirement of any stress measurement method must be to bridge the gap between two, often unrelated, factual circumstances represented by the criteria on which design in rock is based, namely the mechanical rock properties, obtained in many cases by small-scale laboratory test techniques, and the techniques for design in rock often embodying assumptions as to the continuity of massive rock. The stress measurement must therefore ideally be concerned with rock exposures of approximately the same dimensions as the tests on which the design is based (say 2·5 cm boreholes). In this way stress anomalies due to unforeseen environmental or massive structural features in the rock can be obtained with a degree of accuracy not always possible where stress measurement is dissociated from rock test procedures.

12.1 Mechanics of Stress Measurement

The actual concept of stress (Chapter 2), except in terms of a specific load applied to a finite surface, is theoretical. It is therefore difficult to measure stress directly, and to obtain a value for the stress at a point it is normally necessary to measure other properties of the material which can be related to the stress. This approach may be unsatisfactory since it involves generalized assumptions as to the nature of the rock, except in cases where an empirical relationship can be obtained between a particular rock property and the stress within the rock. Such relationships have been obtained in the case of seismic and electrical rock properties, but these have limited application since they cannot be used to determine stress directions, and are often unrelated to previous knowledge.

There are also various indirect methods of measuring stress. These may involve the relief and then restoration of the stress present in rock, by the application of pressures equal to the stresses relieved, the coating of the rock with a birefringent material which will demonstrate the photo-stress conditions in the rock, or the inclusion of a rigid stress-meter with calibrated deformation characteristics. The standard approach to stress measurement is, however, the assumption of elasticity, relating stress and strain in a rock.

It has been shown in Chapter 2 that strain at a point may be represented by nine normal and tangential strain components (ε and γ respectively), viz.:

$$\begin{matrix} \varepsilon_x, & \gamma_{xy}, & \gamma_{xz} \\ \gamma_{yx}, & \varepsilon_y, & \gamma_{yz} \\ \gamma_{zx}, & \gamma_{zy}, & \varepsilon_z \end{matrix} \qquad (21.1)$$

As in the case of a three-dimensional stress system, these may be resolved into three principal strains ε_1, ε_2, ε_3, mutually perpendicular to each other and inclined at the same angles as the principal stresses to the vertical and horizontal X, Y, Z axes.

Thus a series of six strain measurements will determine in a three-dimensional stress field the directions of the principal stresses (assuming isotropy) and the magnitude of the strain (elongation or contraction) in each of these directions. These strain measurements can then be used to determine the values of the principal stresses using known or assumed values of the modulus of elasticity and Poisson's ratio (eqns 3.6, 3.7 and 3.8).

$$\left.\begin{array}{l} \varepsilon_2 = \dfrac{1}{E}[\sigma_1 - \nu(\sigma_2 + \sigma_3)] \\[2mm] \varepsilon_2 = \dfrac{1}{E}[\sigma_2 - \nu(\sigma_1 + \sigma_3)] \\[2mm] \varepsilon_3 = \dfrac{1}{E}[\sigma_3 - \nu(\sigma_1 + \sigma_2)] \end{array}\right\} \qquad (12.2)$$

An important factor in the measurement of strain (or stress) at a point is the number of readings required. It is not impossible in practice to obtain the ideal of six readings, but if simplifying assumptions can be made regarding one of the principal strains this number can be considerably reduced.

The simplifying assumptions usually made to facilitate *in-situ* strain measurement include:

(i) that the major principal strain ε_1 is vertical,
(ii) that the intermediate and minor principal strains ε_2, ε_3 are equal,
(iii) that the directions of the minor and intermediate principal strains are parallel and normal to the measuring face.

This reduces the measurement problem to one concerning two strains of known orientation, in which case only two measurements are required, namely the magnitudes of ε_1 and of $\varepsilon_2/\varepsilon_3$. It is, however, relatively easy to measure the directions of principal strain, if these are required.

12.2 Direct Strain Measurement

The simplest method of direct strain measurement consists of bonding strain gauges to an exposed surface. A strain gauge takes many forms but essentially consists of a length of fine wire or foil formed or stamped onto a paper or plastic base, so that most of its length lies in one direction (1 or 2 cm long). When the gauge is strained axially, the length of the wire extends or contracts, altering the resistance of the gauge. The change in resistance and strain may be related through a gauge factor G, thus:

$$G = \frac{\mathrm{d}R/R}{\mathrm{d}L/L} = \frac{\mathrm{d}R/R}{\varepsilon} \qquad (12.3)$$

where $\mathrm{d}R$ is the change in resistance R and ε is the applied strain.

When the gauge is bonded to a rock, this factor must be adjusted to allow for the effect of the bonding cement – normally an epoxy resin or dental cement, chosen for its similarity to the rock property. In this case:

$$G_B = \frac{G}{1 + \frac{0.04t}{l}\left(1 + v_B\right)\frac{E_w}{E_B}} \tag{12.4}$$

where G_B is the bonded gauge factor, t is the thickness of the bonding cement layer, l is the length of wire, and v_B, E_B, E_w are elastic constants for the bond and wire respectively.

For correct reading, the bonding cement should cover the whole of the gauge base. The output of the strain gauge is normally read by incorporating it into a Wheatstone-bridge circuit with equal resistances in each arm (dummy gauges) and supplied at constant voltage V. Then the voltage output (dv) is equal to:

$$dv = \frac{V\,dR}{4R}\left(1 - \frac{dR}{R}\right) \tag{12.5}$$

which, since dR is small, becomes

$$dv = \frac{V\,dR}{4R} = \frac{VG_B\varepsilon}{4} \tag{12.6}$$

hence,
$$\varepsilon = \frac{4\,dv}{G_B V} \tag{12.7}$$

Strain gauges can be used to measure strain and thence stress either on a two-dimensional surface or in a borehole, provided the direction of one of the principal strains is assumed. Various devices (Leeman, 1964) can be used to introduce strain gauges into a borehole, but basically their use on the flattened end of a borehole is merely the extension of the surface into a rock mass.

The simplest type of device, originally developed by Mohr, consists of a rosette of gauges cemented onto the flattened end of a borehole (Figure 12.1), which is then overcored, the core being removed to the laboratory where the bonding can be inspected and the relieved strain measured. This process can be repeated in the same hole until a picture of the stresses acting in a particular direction from the sidewall is obtained. As a rapid method of obtaining *absolute strain* this method is unequalled. Its accuracy is, however, open to question and Leeman (1964) suggests that gauge measurement may give strain readings up to 1·5 times the actual principal strain values.

The theoretical analysis of strain as measured through a strain-gauge rosette has been discussed in Section 2.3, culminating in eqns (2.17), giving the principal strains and directions. These can be converted to stress through eqn (12.2).

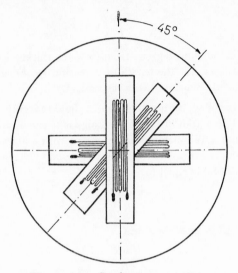

Figure 12.1   Strain-gauge rosette.

12.3 Borehole Strain Measurement

Although *changes in strain* may be measured relatively easily by attaching strain gauges to the face of a borehole, or longitudinally along a borehole, there remains some doubt attached to the accuracy of the results obtained, particularly over a period of time, and there must also be reservations as to the efficiency of accurately attaching a sensitive device at a point remote from the operator. Since the accuracy of bonding is basic to the usefulness of strain gauges, there must always be a question-mark against their use in boreholes, however sophisticated the method of installation, and this can only be overcome by a multiplicity of observations.

For this reason, a method of borehole strain measurement based on the deformation of the borehole itself is found to be more satisfactory for isolated strain measurements, particularly of change in strain. For instance, a borehole subject to an increase in stress will be flattened to an elliptical shape with the major axis of the ellipse normal to the direction of major principal stress. In extreme cases (Figure 12.2), this will result in induced tensile fracture at the ends of the major axis and

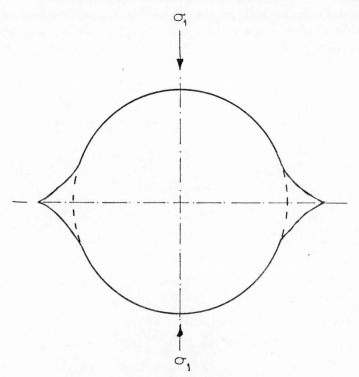

Figure 12.2   Induced tensile fracture in borehole.

evidence of such fracture can often be used to estimate the direction of
the major principal stress.

The general equation for the change in diameter of a circular borehole across a diameter D inclined at an angle θ to the axis of the major
principal stress can be derived from the theory of elasticity as follows:

$$\delta D = \frac{D}{E}[\sigma_1 + \sigma_2 - v\sigma_3 + 2(\sigma_1 - \sigma_2)(1 - v^2) \cos 2\theta] \quad (12.8)$$

where δD is the change in diameter D,

v, E are the elastic constants of the rock which is assumed to be
an isotropic, homogeneous continuous elastic medium,

and σ_1, σ_2, σ_3 are the principal stresses, σ_1, σ_2 assumed normal to
the borehole axis and σ_3 parallel to it.

Apart from assumptions of elasticity, this analysis also of course
assumes that σ_3 is parallel to the borehole axis. If there is any doubt of
this, a second borehole at right angles will be required. The advantage

of this analysis is that by measurement of four changes in diameter, with different values of θ, a solution can be obtained for the four unknowns σ_1, σ_2, σ_3 and θ.

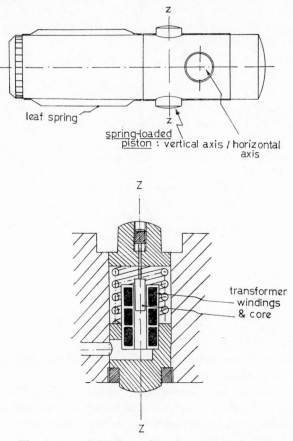

leaf spring

spring-loaded piston : vertical axis / horizontal axis

transformer windings & core

Figure 12.3 C.S.I.R. strain cell. (After Leeman.)

If less information is required, less measurements are needed. Thus if θ is assumed, three measurements will give σ_1, σ_2, σ_3 and if σ_3 is assumed equal to σ_2, two measurements of change in diameter will yield σ_1 and σ_2.

Thus in the simplest form for measurement of a vertical stress σ_1 ($\theta = 0$) and a horizontal stress σ_2 ($\theta = 90°$) eqn (12.8) becomes:

$$\delta D_{2\theta=0,\,180°} = \frac{D}{E}[\sigma_1 + \sigma_2(1 - \nu) + 2(\sigma_1 - \sigma_2)(1 - \nu^2)] \qquad (12.9)$$

This can be further simplified by putting $\theta = 30°$, $\cos 2\theta = 0·5$ and by assuming ν to be small (this may be too large an assumption) in which case:

$$\delta D \simeq \frac{D}{E}(2\sigma_1), \quad \sigma_1 = \frac{E}{2} \cdot \frac{\delta D}{D} \qquad (12.10)$$

Similarly where $\theta = 120°$

$$\sigma_2 = \frac{E}{2} \cdot \frac{\delta D}{D} \qquad (12.11)$$

Several *strain cells* have been devised to measure the deformation in boreholes (Leeman, 1964). Generally these take the form of a spring-loaded pin or piston device in a body which is held in the borehole by leaf springs (Figure 12.3). The movement of the piston is recorded electrically and the deflection obtained from a calibration chart.

It should be noted that since the borehole is assumed stable when the strain cell is inserted, the device can only be successfully used to measure change in stress. Although it can be adapted by prestressing or overcoring to measure absolute stress, it is doubtful whether it could be used for this purpose with the same degree of simplicity or accuracy as strain gauges.

12.4 Absolute Stress Related to Rock Properties

The difficulties and pitfalls inherent in conversion of strain measurements in rock to realistic assessments of the stress field acting on a rock mass, can often lend attraction to more direct methods of stress measurement, particularly in the cases least suitable for isolated measurements, represented by rock at depth subject to high and rapidly changing stress levels or strongly foliated near surface masses. In such a case it may well be profitable to utilize the empirical relationships existing between hydrostatic stress and rock properties – notably electrical resistivity and seismic wave velocity.

The *electrical resistivity* of a rock is affected by many factors, in particular mineral content, structure (particularly pore space) and moisture content. It is especially sensitive to change in mineral content as shown by Young (1963), who measured resistivities ranging from 1–7 Ω-cm in different samples of quartz-pyrites ores. However, this may not have been particularly representative, because of the high conductivity of the pyrites, and there is reason to suppose that consistent values could be obtained for a quasi-homogeneous rock of the type normally surrounding ore-bodies.

The effect of hydrostatic confining pressure on the electrical resistance of solids other than rocks has been investigated in detail by Bridgman (1932), who has found a fairly consistent non-linear inverse relationship between electrical resistance and pressure in the case of all metals. This work has not been extended widely to rocks, although Isaacson (1962) quotes experimental work conducted on the hornblende schists of the Kolar gold-field which yields a similar type of relationship (Figure 12.4). There is no reason to believe that this is not typical of the electrical resistance/stress relationship for a homogeneous (quasi-elastic) type of rock and if this is so, the very high gradient of the curve would suggest a useful method of stress measurement.

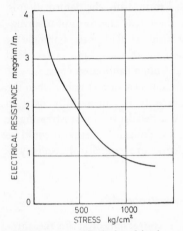

Figure 12.4 Relationship between electrical resistance and stress – horneblende schist. (After Isaacson.)

Difficulties encountered in measuring absolute stress by this method concern mainly the accurate placement of boreholes, the bonding of the ohmeter electrodes and the difficulty of calibration for tectonic stress conditions.

A more widely used method of determining absolute stress is based on the relationship between the *seismic wave velocity* and stress in rock. The seismic wave has two body-wave components, the P-wave (compression) and S-wave (shear), the velocity of each being related to a greater or lesser extent, depending on the elasticity of the rock to its elastic constants (eqns 6.8 and 6.9):

$$C_p = \sqrt{\left[\frac{E(1 - v)g}{\rho(1 + v)(1 - 2v)} \right]} \qquad (12.12)$$

$$C_s = \sqrt{\left[\frac{Eg}{2\rho(1 + v)} \right]} \qquad (12.13)$$

Thus any changes in E, ρ or v due to increasing stress will be reflected in the measured values of C_p and C_s. In actual fact at the stress levels recorded under normal tectonic stress conditions ρ, v are not significantly affected, but the modulus of elasticity does increase slightly with increasing stress in porous rocks, resulting in a slightly increased seismic wave velocity with increased loading.

Whereas the measurement of electrical resistance may be satisfactory in continuous homogeneous (quasi-elastic) rocks, seismic measurements are only suitable in relatively porous (semi-, non-elastic) rock (such as sandstones) in which a relatively large increase in wave velocity is obtained with increasing stress. The difference can be seen in examples quoted by Leeman (1964) and Gregory (1962) (Figure 12.5). These show that fine-grained near-homogeneous quartzite or diabase rock has a relatively consistent wave velocity at all stress levels, whilst a comparatively porous sandstone has a steadily increasing wave velocity with increasing stress.

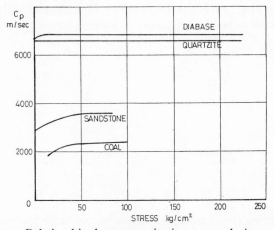

Figure 12.5   Relationship between seismic wave velocity and stress. (After Leeman.)

The major difficulty in the determination of stress from measurements of seismic wave velocity lies in the calibration, which must be performed in the laboratory. For this reason only P-waves are normally considered, and the rock is calibrated by passing single pulses along the axis of an axially loaded cylinder at different stress levels.

12.5 Indirect Stress Measurement

The principle of stress measurement may be applied rather more selectively through some of the various methods of indirect stress measurement. These methods are essentially strain measurement techniques, but may be calibrated in such a way as to give a reading in terms of stress. For this reason, like the methods of strain measurement in the previous sections, they rely to a large extent on the assumed elasticity of the rock, and must where possible be scaled to the laboratory tests upon which values of elastic constants and strengths used as design criteria have been based.

The method of stress measurement using *hydraulic jacks* is based on the relief of stress – say in the sidewall of an excavation – and the recovery of the relieved stress by means of hydraulic pressure. The method is extremely simple and is effective in hard, continuous rocks displaying marked quasi-elastic properties, and ideally may be used in conjunction with similar *in-situ* stress/strain tests (Section 7.6).

The apparatus consists of a metal container made either of copper or aluminium which can be fitted into a slot cut into the rock wall and then filled with oil to pressures up to 1,000 kg/cm². Before cutting the slot

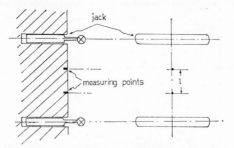

Figure 12.6   Flat-jack stress measurement.

two measuring points are fixed in a line normal to the plane of the slot and level with its centre (Figure 12.6). These may take the form of pegs, grooves or strain gauges and the distance between them (l) is accurately measured. The measuring points should normally be within a distance of one-third of the slot length from the slot for full stress relief.

When the slot is cut and the stress relieved in the immediate area, the distance (l) is expanded by an amount dl. If the jack is then fixed in the slot and the oil pressure in it increased until it reaches parity with the original stress (σ_z), the measuring points should return to their original position and the reading on the pressure gauge will represent the stress in the direction normal to the jack. This may be checked by inserting a further jack in another slot cut at the other side of the measuring points.

Known as the *flat-jack* method, this is a simple way of obtaining vertical and horizontal absolute stresses around an exposed face. Since these are normally the most important stresses in rock engineering, this method is adequate for many applications. It is not, however, a method which can be used to measure stresses within a rock mass. To accomplish this Jaeger and Cook (1963) have developed a *curved-jack* technique for use in boreholes.

Strictly speaking, the curved-jack technique is limited to a depth of about 20 feet from a surface, which has the advantage of enabling the jack to operate with certainty in sound unbroken rock – a particular drawback of the flat jack in rocks which may have been highly stressed at an exposed surface by explosive action. The curved-jack technique has an additional advantage in that it may be studied theoretically, whereas flat jacks are essentially empirical. Curved jacks are basically thin elongated flat jacks which are curved to fit into a diamond drill groove of sufficient length to accommodate the jacks at the base of the hole. Initially a relatively small hole is drilled and two jacks are placed opposite each other on the horizontal axis (Figure 12.7a) so that they occupy two quadrants of the hole. If this hole is bored parallel to one of the principal stresses (say σ_3) it can be shown that if the pressure is increased until indirect tensile failure is induced, then the lines of failure (Figure 12.7b) will indicate the directions of the other principal stresses σ_1, σ_2, in a manner similar to the indirect tensile test. Normally, however, the principal stress directions are assumed and the jacks are pumped to an arbitrary pressure (p_1). The whole system is then overcored using a diamond drill of a large diameter. This has the effect of destressing the original jacks, and four further jacks are placed in the new groove (Figure 12.7c) and their pressure increased to a pressure (p_2) at which pressure (p_1) is restored in the original two jacks. It can then be shown that

$$p_2 = \frac{a^2}{b^2}p_1 + \frac{1}{2}\left(\sigma_1 + \sigma_2\right)\left(1 - \frac{a^2}{b^2}\right) \qquad (12.14)$$

where a, b are respectively the internal and external diameters, and σ_1, σ_2 are the vertical and horizontal principal stresses.

Since it is only possible to take one measurement in each hole, a relationship between σ_1, σ_2 must be assumed and this may be a serious drawback to the method.

The *photoelastic* method of stress determination at a surface has a direct analogy with the strain-gauge method of Section 12.2 and consists of bonding a birefrigent coating backed by a reflecting surface onto a rock face. This can be used to measure change in stress or, by relief through overcoring, to measure absolute stress at a surface. It is limited to surface applications in hard rock and will supply the same information

L

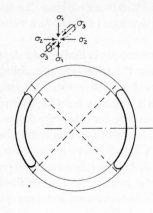

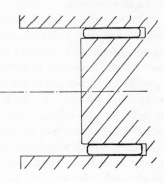

(a)

induced failure

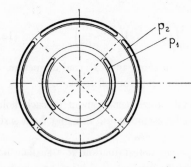

(b)

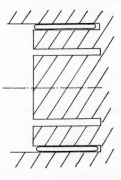

p_2
p_1

(c)

Figure 12.7 Curved jack.

as strain gauges similarly mounted, but in a simpler way. The principles of photoelasticity are described elsewhere (Hendry, 1966). By looking through a polaroid analyser at the photoelastic coating, illuminated by a lamp shining through a crossed polarizer, a stress fringe pattern can be seen on the coating. This can be studied in the laboratory if a core including the coated surface is removed. By inserting quarter wave plates in front of circular polarizers it is possible to estimate from the fringe pattern not only the directions of the two principal stresses but also their magnitude. Because of the poor stability of the plastics normally used for coating, this method is probably better used for absolute stress measurement rather than change in stress.

Because the photoelastic coating technique is suitable only for surface measurements, it is of doubtful value in rocks subject to surface spalling

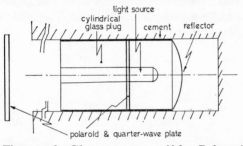

Figure 12.8   Glass stressmeter. (After Roberts.)

or fracture. An improvement suggested by Roberts *et al.* (1964) takes the form of a glass plug inserted in a borehole (Figure 12.8). Like the curved-jack improvement this is suitable for indirect stress measurements some distance away from the surface inside a rock mass and can be used to obtain two stress magnitudes and directions in the assumed direction of a third stress.

The photoelastic plug is one of a family of indirect stress measuring devices, known as *stressmeters*, which may be used to measure stress in a borehole. They are normally designed to fit a borehole exactly and are slightly prestressed or cemented into the borehole so that any increase in stress around the borehole is transmitted to the stressmeter. Glass records the stress through its birefringent properties – other devices (Leeman, 1964) use hydraulic pressure or the electrical or magnetic properties of the stressmeter material to measure increases in stress. Although they can be treated theoretically, the usual method of calibration is through a laboratory test on a stressmeter included in a rock sample. This is sometimes open to question since underground stresses can rarely be accurately simulated in the laboratory.

A further drawback is that stressmeters, designed to measure an increase in stress, can only be adapted with difficulty for absolute stress measurement or where a decrease in stress or a tensile stress might be expected.

Where stressmeters do have an advantage over other devices is when the effective modulus of elasticity of the stressmeter material is very much in excess of the presumed elastic modulus of the rock. In such a case it is possible to ignore the elasticity of the rock, provided the stressmeter calibration is accurate, and thus by-pass some of the fundamental objections to strain measurement in rock as a means of stress determination. In particular this is an advantage in an inhomogeneous non-elastic rock with considerable variations in its mechanical properties, and for such a rock a stressmeter may be a suitable method for measuring approximate change in stress.

13

Design in Rock

A knowledge of basic rock properties can be applied to problems of design in rock by comparing experimentally obtained failure criteria with design stresses which have been calculated from assumed rock reactions based on observed deformation criteria. In conventional structural materials, calculations of design stresses are normally based on the theory of elasticity, the major mathematical tool of the structural engineer. This approach may also be used as a basis for design in rock if stresses are reasonably low and the rock has no macro-structural features.

Even the theory of elasticity, however, has limitations when the structure takes on an unusual geometrical shape – a common procedure in rock engineering – and in this case model studies (usually of gelatine) can be used to estimate stress distribution. In this chapter, which introduces briefly some of the more important design processes, criteria for design are summarized and classified and the method of mathematical and model analysis in the design process is outlined.

13.1 Classification of Design Criteria

In Chapter 1 a geological classification of rocks based on origin and mineral content was briefly discussed. Whilst useful in a general way in indicating certain strength parameters, such a classification provides little information of immediate use to the engineer designing in rock, who requires a functional classification of design criteria based on mechanical properties. Such a classification must include information on the deformation characteristics of the rock, its strength and failure characteristics and its natural state. Perhaps the most successful classification of this nature has been introduced by Coates (1964, 1965, 1966), who bases his classification on uniaxial compressive strength. He defines rocks as strong or weak with a dividing line of 700 kg/cm^2 and elastic or yielding, depending respectively on whether the permanent strain is less or greater than 25%, or the creep rate is less or greater than 5×10^{-7} cm/sec at stress levels equivalent to half the compressive strength of the rock. Thus a quartzite might be described as a strong elastic rock and design based on elastic theory, and a shale described as a weak yielding rock and design concentrated on support systems.

Coates's approach may usefully be extended to emphasize the importance of the *deformation characteristics* of the rock as a design parameter in preference to the strength and yield capacity of the rock which can in many ways be related to them.

The majority of theoretical analyses of stress in rock are based on an assumption that the rock obeys the theory of elasticity, and reacts to its force environment as a brittle elastic solid, failing when the confining stresses combine to exceed the failure strength of the rock in the plane of maximum shear. This is excellent when the rock has quasi-elastic properties, but when it is self-evidently non-elastic, large errors can arise. A primary definition in any classification of rock properties must therefore concern the reaction of the rock to deformation-inducing forces. Such a definition was introduced in Chapter 3 where it was shown that rocks could be divided roughly into three classes: *quasi-elastic, semi-elastic* and *non-elastic* according to the linearity of their unconfined stress/strain relationship, which is respectively, linear, curvilinear and non-linear. The quasi-elastic and semi-elastic rock may in this case be described as brittle; the non-elastic rocks exhibit considerable flow under prefailure stresses.

It is therefore advisable in the initial stages of any rock investigation to conduct a full stress/strain test, although an indication of the elastic properties of a rock may be obtained from the *initial tangent modulus of elasticity* which does, however, overlap slightly from one form to another. Thus the initial tangent modulus of a quasi-elastic rock lies normally between 6 and 11×10^5 kg/cm^2 and of a semi-elastic rock between 4 and 7×10^5 kg/cm^2. Any rock with a modulus of elasticity below 5×10^5 kg/cm^2 is likely to be non-elastic and will flow at prefailure stress levels – a factor which must also be considered in many semi-elastic rocks.

There are many ways of stating *flow* in a rock – either through percentage strain over a period of applied stress, instantaneous strain rate under defined stress and time conditions, or even as a coefficient of viscosity. However, perhaps the most satisfactory is in terms of the *creep constant* (Chapter 4) (or *creep exponent*), under defined stress conditions, which may be quoted singly to define the reactions of a non-elastic rock under load, or in conjunction with the modulus of elasticity to estimate the reactions of a semi-elastic rock. Normally under a stress differential of 100 kg/cm^2 a creep constant value of 10^{-6} or less denotes insignificant flow while a creep constant of 10^{-4} or more will presage large-scale flow in the rock. Intermediate values will indicate flow to a greater or lesser extent depending on the magnitude of the applied stress, reducing to zero flow (quasi-elastic conditions) at low stress levels.

To define fully the elastic deformation of a rock, a value is also required for *Poisson's ratio*. It is possible to obtain a value from tests for this constant; but accuracy is often sacrificed either through inaccurate measurement of small lateral deformation, or unjustified assumptions in dynamic tests. Invariably an accurate test on a quasi-elastic or semi-elastic rock produces a value for Poisson's ratio in the region of 0·25. Any value below this in non-elastic rocks (or above 0·33) is completely unrealistic and can indicate only an inaccurate test or a non-elastic rock. Where design based on elastic theory is envisaged therefore, an assumption of 0·25 for Poisson's ratio is entirely justified.

Strength as a rock property is of paramount importance in design in quasi- and semi-elastic rocks and is important in non-elastic rocks subject to high instantaneous or short-term loading.

The strength of a rock (Chapter 5) under all loading conditions may be defined in terms of its *uniaxial compressive, uniaxial tensile* and *uniaxial shear* strengths and its angle or coefficient of *internal friction*. In most rocks these four properties may be related accurately in the Coulomb–Navier failure criterion through the compressive/tensile strength ratio, approximately equal to 10 in quasi-elastic rocks, 6 in semi-elastic rocks and 4 in non-elastic rocks. For accurate analysis, however, equivalent information may be obtained from a triaxial test which will also indicate any reduction in the coefficient of internal friction at high confining pressures.

All rock properties, and particularly strength, are affected by the presence of water in the rock pores. Any strength classification must therefore include an indication of the porosity and the percentage saturation of a rock. In quasi-elastic rocks with low porosity this has less importance than in semi-elastic and non-elastic rocks where water can reduce strength or increase flow.

A further adjustment must be made in cases where rocks are subject to dynamic loading, when apart from calculations of dynamic load on a structure, assessments of rate of loading and its effect on other rock properties including strength must be made.

Structural features of rock masses are an important factor in any consideration of rock properties in so far as they normally represent a plane or series of planes of weakness in the rock. In igneous rocks, common structures normally take the form of joints or faults, and in metamorphic and sedimentary rocks, foliation surfaces, joints and faults. Joints and foliation surfaces are often mutually parallel and at right angles to each other and may be defined, where accuracy is required, in terms of *strike direction, spacing* and *inclination*. However, under normal circumstances it is sufficient to define a rock in terms of its *massive* state and degree of

TABLE 13.1 Essential Rock Properties

(1) Mode of deformation	*Quasi-elastic, semi-elastic* or *non-elastic*	
and elasticity/flow parameters	Modulus of elasticity	E
	Creep constant	A
	(at known stress difference)	
(2) Strength parameters	Uniaxial compressive strength	S_c
	Uniaxial tensile strength	S_T
	Uniaxial shear strength	S_s
	Coefficient of internal friction	μ
(3) Massive state	*Continuous* or *foliated*	
	Joint spacing	b_j
	Joint strike direction	γ_j
	Joint inclination to vertical	β_j
	Joint friction coefficient	μ_j
	Joint shear resistance	S_{R_j}
	Foliation spacing	b_f
	Foliation direction	γ_f
	Foliation inclination	β_f
	Foliation friction coefficient	μ_f
	Foliation shear resistance	S_{R_f}
(4) Additional information	As required by environmental and loading conditions (porosity n_a, saturation a, etc.)	

TABLE 13.2 Basic Rock Properties

(1) Mode of deformation and elasticity/flow parameters	*Quasi-, semi-* or *non-elastic*	
	Modulus of elasticity	E
	Creep constant	A
	(at known stress difference)	
(2) Strength parameter	Uniaxial compressive strength	S_c
(3) Massive state	Continuous or foliated Narrow, medium or wide joint/foliation separation	

joint/foliation separation (Chapter 10). Faults are normally inclined to the vertical and can be defined in terms of *strike direction* and *inclination*.

The importance of a structural weakness plane lies in its *shear resistance* and *friction coefficient* as compared with the shear strength and coefficient of internal friction of the rock mass under similar load conditions, and also the angle between the weakness plane and the plane of major shear stress in the rock.

TABLE 13.3   Typical Rock Property Classification

Rock:	Granite	Limestone	Shale
Mode of Deformation	Quasi-elastic	Semi-elastic	Non-elastic
E kg/cm^2	9.5×10^5	6.2×10^5	—
A	2×10^{-6} (at 100 kg/cm^2)	1.5×10^{-5} (at 100 kg/cm^2)	3×10^{-3} (at 100 kg/cm^2)
S_c kg/cm^2	2,400	1,700	600
S_T kg/cm^2	370	280	150
S_s kg/cm^2	500	330	150
μ	1.5	1.0	0.7
Massive state	Continuous	Stratified	Stratified
b_j metres	4	1	0.02
γ_j	N 40° E	N 25° W	N 5° E
β_j	5°	15°	10°
μ_j	1.4	0.8	0.5
S_{R_j} kg/cm^2	400	170	80
b_f metres	—	10	0.2
γ_f	—	N 65° E	N 85° W
β_f	—	75°	80°
μ_f	—	0.8	0.4
S_{R_f} kg/cm^2	—	160	85
n_a %	1.0	8	25
a %	10	90	100

Values of shear resistance and coefficient of friction of discontinuities depend to a very large extent on the type and width of a joint, foliation surface or fault and in particular on any infilling material. Normally, however, large-scale shear tests can be arranged (see Chapter 7) where accuracy is required, or the values may be taken as approximately 50% of rock values.

Joint and foliation spacing varies widely with the type of rock, but is often assumed proportional to rock strength varying from the order of metres in quasi-elastic rock down to centimetres in non-elastic rock (Chapter 10).

A detailed rock classification will therefore include information under three major headings concerning *deformation* and *strength* characteristics and the *massive state* of the rock (Tables 13.1–2). This is sufficient to define the rock first as a material and then as a mass. Basically it contains all the information which an engineer will need to design in rocks under optimum static load conditions (see also Table 13.3).

Additional information which may be required under specified environmental conditions and loading conditions other than static may be added as required. This would concern the likely effects of water or of rate and magnitude of loading on the mechanical properties.

The information contained in Table 13.1 may be rather too detailed for competent rocks where sufficient information can be obtained from empirical relationships between the various rock properties. In this case the basic information quoted in Table 13.2 should be sufficient.

13.2 Mathematical Analysis

If a rock fails as a brittle material (quasi- or semi-elastic rock) any design analysis must centre on a calculation of the maximum values of tensile and compressive (and resultant shear) stresses acting in any part of a structure, and the comparison of these values with the relevant tensile, compressive or shear strengths of the structural rock. There are two basic methods of completing this design analysis, namely through reference to a mathematical model or to a physical model (Section 13.3).

Obviously, the variety of physical and mechanical variables associated with rock as a structural material do not readily lend themselves to simple mathematical simulation, and to obtain a readily understandable and soluble mathematical model it is often necessary to make sweeping assumptions as to the mechanical state of the rock, particularly concerning its deformaton characteristics and apparent massive state. Thus for a simple mathematical model utilizing the theory of elasticity (Chapters 2, 3), the following assumptions are necessary:

(i) There must be a *linear* relationship between stress and strain (cf. Figure 3.3) in the rock.

(ii) The rock must be *homogeneous* – meaning that structural discontinuities must be small in relation to the total scale of the model.

(iii) The rock must be *isotropic*, an impossible stipulation in the case of thinly bedded or laminated rock.

(iv) The rock must be perfectly *elastic*, and applied loads must be sufficiently low to allow instant recovery of all deformations on removal of the deforming loads.

These assumptions are, of course, unsupportable except as a near approximation, although inhomogeneities or anisotropies may be allowed for in the mathematical solution, by subdividing the model into elements, so that the forces and resultant displacements at the boundary of each element may be obtained and assembled into a particular directional form (Zienkiewicz and Cheung, 1966).

Basically, a mathematical model of an assumed elastic prototype must incorporate the assumed deformation characteristics of the rock, the size and shape of the structure envisaged and the boundary conditions surrounding it, stated in terms of applied forces and/or displacements and body forces (density), where these are considered significant. For a correct solution these must determine (Chapter 2) in a three-dimensional state: six stress components (σ_x, σ_y, σ_z, τ_{xy}, τ_{yz}, τ_{zx}), six strain components (ε_x, ε_y, ε_z, γ_{xy}, γ_{yz}, γ_{zx}), and three displacement components (u, v, w); and in a two-dimensional state: three stress components (σ_x, σ_y, τ_{xy}), three strain components (ε_x, ε_y, γ_{xy}), and two displacement components (u, v).

The latter case of plane stress/strain represents the more simple application and may be resolved by considering the various conditions which must be fulfilled for solution of a problem involving elasticity. These are represented by:

(i) stress/strain relationship:

$$\varepsilon_x = \frac{1}{E}(\sigma_x - \nu\sigma_y)$$

$$\varepsilon_y = \frac{1}{E}(\sigma_y - \nu\sigma_x) \qquad (13.1)$$

$$\gamma_{xy} = \frac{\tau_{xy}}{G}$$

(ii) strain displacement relationship:

$$\varepsilon_x = \frac{\partial u}{\partial x}, \quad \varepsilon_y = \frac{\partial v}{\partial y}, \quad \gamma_{xy} = \frac{\partial u}{\partial y} + \frac{\partial v}{\partial x} \qquad (13.2)$$

(iii) conditions for equilibrium:

$$\frac{\partial \sigma_x}{\partial x} + \frac{\partial \tau_{xy}}{\partial y} + X = 0$$

$$\frac{\partial \sigma_y}{\partial y} + \frac{\partial \tau_{xy}}{\partial x} + Y = 0$$

(13.3)

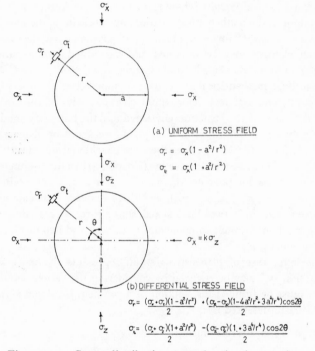

(a) UNIFORM STRESS FIELD

$$\sigma_r = \sigma_x(1 - a^2/r^2)$$
$$\sigma_t = \sigma_x(1 + a^2/r^2)$$

(b) DIFFERENTIAL STRESS FIELD

$$\sigma_r = \frac{(\sigma_z + \sigma_x)(1 - a^2/r^2)}{2} + \frac{(\sigma_z - \sigma_x)(1 - 4a^2/r^2 + 3a^4/r^4)\cos 2\theta}{2}$$

$$\sigma_t = \frac{(\sigma_z + \sigma_x)(1 + a^2/r^2)}{2} - \frac{(\sigma_z - \sigma_x)(1 + 3a^4/r^4)\cos 2\theta}{2}$$

Figure 13.1 Stress distribution around a circular opening.

(iv) conditions for compatibility:

$$\frac{\partial^2 \varepsilon_x}{\partial y^2} + \frac{\partial^2 \varepsilon_y}{\partial x^2} = \frac{\partial^2 \gamma_{xy}}{\partial x \partial y}$$

(13.4)

(v) boundary conditions:
specified by surface stress components X, Y and resultant displacements u, v.

These may be combined by use of the Laplace transformation to form groups of simultaneous partial differential equations in terms of σ_x, σ_y or ε_x, ε_y and referred to rectangular co-ordinates x, y – representing an extremely difficult solution, except where symmetry allows superposition of the structural boundaries and force directions onto a particular co-ordinate system (i.e. circular structure on polar co-ordinates).

Several classical solutions by this method having a wide application in rock engineering are illustrated in Figures 13.1 and 13.2.

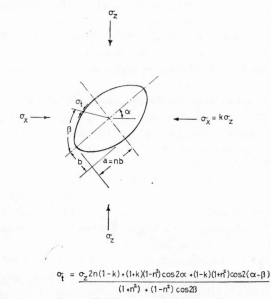

$$\sigma_t = \frac{\sigma_z 2n(1-k) + (1+k)(1-n^2)\cos2\alpha + (1-k)(1+n^2)\cos2(\alpha-\beta)}{(1+n^2) + (1-n^2)\cos2\beta}$$

Figure 13.2 Stress distribution around an elliptical opening.

13.3 Model Analysis

The extreme difficulties involved in mathematical analysis of non-symmetrical structures lend particular attraction to the use of models as a means of solving problems associated with design in rock. However, this does not mean that for acceptable quantitative data the model analysis may be less rigorous than a mathematical analysis.

Although an arbitrarily selected model will often give results which appear to represent satisfactorily the conditions in a prototype situation, it is unlikely that sufficiently accurate correlation will be obtained, unless the variables relating the model and prototype have been equated by *dimensional analysis*. To achieve this, it is essential that the fundamental characteristics of both model and prototype are motivated by the same physical reactions. Thus in the case of a model designed to measure the stress conditions in, and subsequent displacements about, a subsurface structure, an essential requirement is the assumption of quasi-elastic deformation.

Since stresses induced in the earth's crust by excavation or construction are not normally of short duration, this implies an acceptance that time-dependent movement is negligible in terms of normal stress values. The same argument would preclude the consideration of temperature effects. It also means that only stresses below the elastic limit may be considered, virtually excluding all situations involving fracture or failure. In such situations similarity is so inconsistent that simple mathematical treatment of empirical and observed data becomes the only satisfactory means of analysis.

Assuming elastic conditions therefore, it may be seen that in related structures, stress (σ) and displacement (δ) at a point will depend on three major factors: the geometry of the structures, the physical properties of the respective materials and the nature of the applied loads, which give a total of five essential variables; *length* (l), *density* (ρ), *modulus of elasticity* (E), *Poisson's ratio* (ν) and the *applied stress* (σ_a). Unless the structures are unidimensional, of uniform material content and subject to uniaxial stress conditions, these variables will be related to the other dimensions, materials, and stresses in the structure by various ratios represented by k_l, k_ρ, k_E, k_ν, and k_{σ_a}.

Buckingham's second theorem is the basis of all dimensional analysis and states briefly that an equation which is dimensionally symmetrical can be reduced to a relationship between dimensionless products. The dimensions of a particular variable are made up of three fundamental dimensional units, length (L), mass (M) and time (t). The main variables in stress analysis can therefore be expressed in dimensional units as in Table 13.4. In addition to the other variables, x', y', z' represent the co-ordinates of the point subject to displacement (δ) on both model and prototype. There are therefore a total of nine independent variables made up of two fundamental dimensional units. Buckingham's first theorem states that the maximum number of *dimensionless groups* is equal to the difference between the number of variables and the number of fundamental dimensions; in this case seven. In other words, of the nine variables, seven may be expressed in terms of the other two to make them dimensionless. Thus from Table 13.4, l and σ_a can be taken as the dividers to give the best set of dimensionless products:

$$\frac{\delta}{l}, \ \frac{\sigma}{\sigma_a}, \ \frac{\rho l}{\sigma_a}, \ \frac{E}{\sigma_a}, \ \frac{x'}{l}, \ \frac{y'}{l}, \ \frac{z'}{l} \qquad (13.5)$$

Since v, k_l, k_ρ, k_E, k_v, $k_{\sigma\hat{a}}$ are already dimensionless they need not be included in the analysis.

All the dimensionless groups can now be substituted into Buckingham's second theorem which in this case reduces the dimensional functions:

$$\sigma, \delta = \mathrm{f}, \mathrm{f}'(l, \rho, E, v, \sigma_a, x', y', z', k_l, k_\rho, k_E, k_v, k_{\sigma\hat{a}}) \qquad (13.6)$$

to:
$$\frac{\sigma}{\sigma_a} = \phi\left(\frac{\rho l}{\sigma_a}, \frac{E}{\sigma_a}, v, \frac{x'}{l}, \frac{y'}{l}, \frac{z'}{l}, k_v, k_\rho, k_E, k_v, k_{\sigma\hat{a}}\right) \qquad (13.7)$$

$$\frac{\delta}{l} = \phi'\left(\frac{\rho l}{\sigma_a} \cdot \ldots \ldots \ldots \ldots \ldots \ldots k_{\sigma\hat{a}}\right) \qquad (13.8)$$

where f, f′, ϕ, ϕ' are indeterminate functions.

TABLE 13.4   Dimensions of main variables

Variable	δ	σ	l	ρ	E	σ_a	x'	y'	z'
Dimensions	L	ML^{-2}	L	ML^{-3}	ML^{-2}	ML^{-2}	L	L	L

For conditions of similarity between model and prototype the arguments of eqns (13.7) and (13.8) must be the same in both situations. This implies firstly that v, independent of all groups, must be exactly the same in both model and prototype – this is particularly important, and having regard to the difficulties in determining v accurately, particularly difficult.

The terms x'/l, y'/l, z'/l mean that the same geometrical point of stress measurement is required for model/prototype similarity, and equality of the constant ratios represented by k_l requires complete geometrical similarity of all dimensions. Similarly, equality in k_ρ, k_E, $k_{\sigma\hat{a}}$ requires similarity of all related material properties and of all applied stresses. Lateral stress in particular, represented by $k_{\sigma\hat{a}}$, must be equated to lateral stress in the prototype.

The two terms in which some latitude is permissible are the modulus of elasticity E, dependent on the magnitude of the stress – this implies that only one magnitude of loading may be applied to a particular model – and ρ dependent on stress magnitude and length.

By directly relating various individual groups, without impairing the equality of ϕ, ϕ', various equations can be obtained relating model (denoted by suffix m) and prototype materials. Obviously, the first relates to Poisson's ratio:

$$v_m = v \qquad (13.9)$$

Similarly, for the other material properties the equation takes the form:

$$\frac{E}{E_m} = \frac{\sigma_a}{\sigma_{a_m}} = \frac{\rho}{\rho_m} \cdot \frac{l}{l_m} \qquad (13.10)$$

From eqns (13.9) and (13.10) it is immediately evident that a reduced-scale model made up from the prototype material is quite useless for quantitative and probably also for qualitative work; so are some of the conventional model materials such as sand, plaster-of-Paris and glass.

Since only the modulus of elasticity can be readily reduced in comparison with the prototype material, in order to achieve the desired reduction in scale of dimension and load, the ideal material must have a low modulus of elasticity, while retaining a comparable Poisson's ratio. This reduces the field of materials suitable for simple models in rock engineering to one or two extremely soft materials with roughly elastic properties, such as gelatine and glycerine–gelatine mixtures. What ideally happens with these materials is that models made from them are stressed by their own weight and there is therefore no need to simulate the earth's gravitational field, as would be the case with other materials.

Obviously gelatine is not a convenient material for use in model studies, but it is one of the few materials suitable for massive rock simulation in a simple model. Ideally if any other material is used to model a structure in massive rock, the body forces due to the earth's gravitational field and the gravitational field surrounding the model must be taken into account. It is therefore necessary to introduce, in addition to the variables considered in the simple model, further parameters such as the gravitational acceleration and gravitational forces acting on the model.

Hoek (1965b) has studied the relationships required for model similitude under such conditions, assuming elasticity and thermal equilibrium.

The relationship between Poisson's ratio in each case is unchanged (eqn 13.9), but the relationship between the modulus of elasticity, density and length dimension (eqn 13.10) is of course dependent on *gravitational acceleration* (g):

$$\frac{E}{E_m} = \frac{l}{l_m} \cdot \frac{\rho}{\rho_m} \cdot \frac{g}{g_m} \qquad (13.11)$$

This condition considerably increases the freedom of choice of model material, since if g_m can be increased by several orders then l_m can be decreased by an equivalent order. For instance, if the model is mounted in a centrifuge and subjected to an acceleration equivalent to 100g, the dimension of the model may be reduced by one-hundredth without altering either the modulus of elasticity or the density of the model. In this case either the prototype material, a plaster-of-Paris, or a bi-refringent material for photoelastic studies, can be substituted in the model.

The same conditions of similarity also apply between the stress applied to the model and the modulus of elasticity:

$$\frac{\sigma_a}{\sigma_{am}} = \frac{E}{E_m} = \frac{l}{l_m} \cdot \frac{\rho}{\rho_m} \cdot \frac{g}{g_m} \qquad (13.12)$$

An additional factor introduced by the consideration of gravity is the time scale involved in the subsequent inertia forces, resulting in the equation:

$$\frac{t}{t_m} = \left(\frac{\rho E_m}{\rho_m E}\right)^{\frac{1}{2}} \cdot \frac{l}{l_m} \qquad (13.13)$$

This of course implies that where the prototype material is used in the model, time-dependent effects need not be ignored.

How important is the simulation of gravity? To say that it is essential would invalidate a large proportion of the model work performed in the investigation of design problems in rock, which has largely been conducted on models subject solely to externally applied forces. Hoek(1965b) suggests that such an approximation may be valid for a small excavation in a semi-infinite situation – a problem rarely obtained in rock engineering and one which is relatively amenable to simple stress analysis and theoretical solution.

For more complex situations, such as large, shallow excavations in close proximity, it is doubtful whether a simple model will give results which are closely related to the actual solution. In a similar way a theoretical model of such a situation would involve unjustifiable simplifications to facilitate solution.

It does therefore appear that to justify a model investigation of all save the simplest situations in massive rock, a gelatine model, which approximately simulates gravity, or a model in a centrifuge to physically simulate large gravitational accelerations, is essential. This is particularly important if the induction of fracture in the model is contemplated.

A typical centrifuge, designed by Hoek, is capable of working at accelerations above 1,000g at speeds in the region of 900 r.p.m. on a 1·3 m radius of rotation. This is sufficient acceleration for the study of (i) stresses induced in the elastic range in photoelastic materials and (ii) fractures induced outside the elastic range in brittle materials.

M

The study of brittle fracture is beyond the range of much dimensional analysis, since in such a case the elastic properties of the prototype and model material are meaningless. The important properties are the force field surrounding the model, the dimensions of the model and its strength (S) thus; for approximate similarity:

$$\frac{S}{S_m} = \frac{l}{l_m} \cdot \frac{\rho}{\rho_m} \cdot \frac{g}{g_m} \qquad (13.14)$$

Since the force field is all-important, simple simulation of fracture in an externally loaded model can rarely be justified.

The difficulty – once force, dimension and strength are reconciled – is in simulation of fracture properties. To simulate rock fracture a model material must obviously be granular; but apart from this, considerable difficulties are encountered in selection of material, due to convenience of modelling and other factors. A plaster-of-Paris mixture is normally chosen, since strength can be relatively easily ordered by adjusting the quantity of water in the mixture.

Selected Bibliography

A list of texts, symposia and journals of interest to students and engineers faced with problems involving design in rock.

1. TEXTS

COATES, D. (1966), *Rock Mechanics Principles*, Dept. of Mines & Technical Surveys, Ottawa.

EVANS, I. and POMEROY, C. D. (1966), *Strength, Fracture and Workability of Coal*, Pergamon, Oxford. (277 pp.)

HAST, N. (1958), *Measurement of Rock Pressure in Mines*, Sverige Geol. Unders. Arsbok, 52. (181 pp.)

ISAACSON, E. ST Q. (1962), *Rock Pressure in Mines* (2nd ed.), Mining Publications, London. (260 pp.)

JAEGER, J. C. (1962), *Elasticity, Fracture and Flow* (2nd ed.), Methuen, London. (212 pp.)

JAEGER, J. C. and COOK, N. G. W. (1968), *Fundamentals of Rock Mechanics*, Methuen, London.

KRYNINE, D. P. and JUDD, W. R. (1957), *Engineering Geology and Geotechnics*, McGraw-Hill, New York. (730 pp.)

LANCASTER-JONES, P. F. F. (1966), *Bibliography of Rock Mechanics*, Cementation Company, London. (89 pp.)

OBERT, L. and DUVALL, W. I. (1967), *Rock Mechanics and the Design of Structures in Rock*, Wiley, New York.

PRICE, N. J. (1965), *Fault and Joint Development in Brittle and Semibrittle Rock*, Pergamon, Oxford. (176 pp.)

RAMSAY, J. G. (1967), *Folding and Fracturing of Rocks*, McGraw-Hill, New York. (568 pp.)

REYNOLDS, H. R. (1961), *Rock Mechanics*, Crosby Lockwood, London. (136 pp.)

SZECHY, K. (1966), *The Art of Tunnelling*, Akademiai Kiado, Budapest. (891 pp.)

TALOBRE, J. A. (1957), *La Méchanique des Roches*, Dunod, Paris. (444 pp.)

WOODRUFF, S. (1966), *Methods of Working Coal and Metal Mines*, Vol. 1, Pergamon, Oxford. (580 pp.)

2. SYMPOSIA

International Symposium on Mining Research (ed. G. B. Clarke), Pergamon, Oxford (1962).

3rd International Conference on Strata Control, Rev. Ind. Minérale, Paris (1960).
4th International Conference on Strata Control and Rock Mechanics, Columbia Univ., New York (1964).
8th International Congress on Large Dams (Edinburgh), Vol. 1. Commission Internationale des Grandes Barrages, Paris (1964).
Mechanical Properties of Non-metallic Brittle Materials (ed. W. H. Walton), Butterworths, London (1958).
Proceedings of the 1st Congress (Lisbon), Vols. 1, 2, 3, Int. Society of Rock Mechanics (1966).
State of Stress in the Earth's Crust (ed. W. R. Judd), Elsevier, New York (1964).
4th Symposium on Rock Mechanics (ed. H. Hartmann), *Bull.* **76**, Min. Inds. Exp. Stn, Penn. State Univ. (1961).
Rock Mechanics (5th Symposium, ed. C. Fairhurst), Pergamon, Oxford (1963).
Rock Mechanics in Engineering Practice (ed. O. C. Zienkiewicz and K. G. Stagg), Wiley, New York (1968).
6th Symposium on Rock Mechanics, Univ. Missouri, Rolla (1964).
8th Symposium on Rock Mechanics (ed. C. Fairhurst), Amer. Inst. Min. Eng. (1968).
Symposium on Rock Mechanics (Queens Univ.), Dept. of Mines & Technical Surveys, Ottawa (1964).
Symposium on Rock Mechanics and Strata Control in Mines, S. African Inst. Min. Met., Johannesburg (1966).
Testing Techniques for Rock Mechanics (STP 402), American Society for Testing and Materials, Philadelphia (1966).

3. JOURNALS

International Journal of Rock Mechanics and Mining Sciences (ed. A. Roberts), Pergamon, Oxford (1964–).
Journal of Engineering Geology, Geological Society, London (1967–).
Engineering Geology (ed. F. Donath *et al.*), Elsevier, Amsterdam (1965–).
Geotechnique, Institution of Civil Engineers, London (1951–).
Rock Mechanics and Engineering Geology (ed. L. Muller), International Society of Rock Mechanics, Vienna (1963–).

References

AMERICAN SOCIETY FOR TESTING AND MATERIALS (1966), 'Testing techniques for rock mechanics', *Amer. Soc. Test. Mats., Philadelphia,* S.T.P. No. 402.

ANDERSON, E. M. (1951), *The Mechanics of Faulting*, Oliver & Boyd, Edinburgh.

ATCHISON, T. C. and ROTH, J. (1961), 'Comparative studies of explosives in marble', *U.S. Bureau of Mines, Rept Invest.*, 5797.

ATCHISON, T. C. and TOURNAY, W. E. (1959), 'Comparative studies of explosives in granite', *U.S. Bureau of Mines, Rept Invest.*, 5509.

ATTEWELL, P. B. and FARMER, I. W. (1964a), 'Ground vibrations from blasting, their generation form and detection', *Quarry Man. J.*, **48**, 191.

ATTEWELL, P. B. and FARMER, I. W. (1964b), 'Attenuation of ground vibrations from blasting', *Quarry Man. J.*, **48**, 211.

ATTEWELL, P. B., FARMER, I. W. and HASLAM, D. (1965), 'Prediction of ground vibration parameters from major quarry blasts', *Mining & Minerals Eng.*, **1**, 621.

BERRY, D. C. (1964), 'A theoretical elastic model of the complete region affected by mining a thin seam', *Proc. 6th Symp. Rock Mech., Univ. Missouri, Rolla.*

BIOT, M. A. (1956), 'Theory of propagation of elastic waves in a fluid saturated porous solid. Low frequency range', *J. Acoust. Soc. Amer.*, **28**, 168.

BLAIR, B. E. (1955), 'Physical properties of mine rocks' (3), *U.S. Bureau of Mines, Rept Invest.*, 5130.

BLAIR, B. E. (1956), 'Physical properties of mine rocks' (4), *U.S. Bureau of Mines, Rept Invest.*, 5244.

BOOZER, G. D., HILLER, K. H. and SERDENGECTI, S. (1962), 'Effects of pore fluids on the behaviour of rock subject to triaxial compression.' *Proc. 5th Symp. Rock Mech.*, Pergamon, Oxford.

BRACE, W. F. (1960), 'An extension of the Griffith theory of fracture to rock', *J. Geophys. Res.*, **65**, 3477.

BROWN, P. D. and ROBERTSHAW, J. (1953), '*In-situ* measurement of Young's Modulus for rock by a dynamic method', *Geotechnique*, **3**, 283.

BRYAN, A., BRYAN, J. G. and FOUCHÉ, J. (1964), 'Some problems of strata control and support in pillar workings', *Trans. Inst. Mining Engineers*, **123**, 238.

COATES, D. F. (1964), 'Classification of rocks for rock mechanics', *Int. J. Rock Mech. Min. Sci.*, **1**, 421.

COATES, D. F. (1965), *Rock Mechanics Principles*, Dept. of Mines & Technical Surveys, Ottawa, Mines Branch, Mon. 874.

COATES, D. F. and PARSONS, R. C. (1966), 'Experimental criteria for classification of rock substances', *Int. J. Rock Mech. Min. Sci.*, 3, 181.

COLBACK, P. S. B. and WIID, B. L. (1965), 'Influence of moisture content on the compressive strength of rock', *Proc. Rock Mech. Symp. Can. Dept. Mines & Tech. Surveys*, Ottawa.

D'ANDREA, D. A., FISCHER, R. L. and FOGELSON, D. E. (1965), 'Prediction of compressive strength from other rock properties', *U.S. Bureau of Mines, Rept Invest.*, 6702.

DAVIES, B., FARMER, I. W. and ATTEWELL, P. B. (1964), 'Ground vibrations from shallow sub-surface blasts', *Engineer*, 217, 553.

DE SITTER, L. U. (1957), *Structural Geology*, McGraw-Hill, New York.

DONATH, F. A. (1964), 'Strength variation and deformation behaviour in anisotropic rock', *Symp. State of Stress in the Earth's Crust* (ed. W. R. Judd), Elsevier, New York.

DU BOIS, E. (1963), 'Injections with high pressures in deep mines', *Symp. Grouts & Drilling Muds in Eng. Pract.*, Butterworths, London.

DUNCAN, N. (1965), 'Geology and rock mechanics in civil engineering practice', *Water Power*, 17, 25.

DUNCAN, N. and CHASE, A. S. (1966), 'Rock mechanics in civil engineering works', *Civil Engineering*, 61, 327.

DUVALL, W. I. and PETKOF, B. (1959), 'Spherical propagation of explosive generated strain pulses in rock', *U.S. Bureau of Mines, Rept Invest.*, 5483.

DUVALL, W. I., DEVINE, J. F., JOHNSON, C. F. and MEYER, A. V. (1962), 'Vibration from instantaneous, and milli-second delayed quarry blasts', *U.S. Bureau of Mines, Rept Invest.*, 6151.

FARMER, I. W. (1965), 'New methods of fracturing rock', *Mining & Minerals Eng.*, 1, 177.

FARMER, I. W. (1967), 'Rock fracture by water jet impact', *Colliery Eng.*, 44, 23.

FARMER, I. W. and POOLEY, F. D. (1967), 'A hypothesis to explain the occurrence of outbursts in coal', *Int. J. Rock Mech. Min. Sci.*, 4, 189.

FOOTE, P. (1964), 'An expanding bolt seam tester', *Int. J. Rock Mech. Min. Sci.*, 1, 255.

GREENLAND, B. J. (1961), 'Rock Mechanics', *Colliery Guardian*, 346, 203.

GREGORY, A. R. (1962), 'Shear wave velocity measurement of elastic waves in a fluid saturated porous solid', *Proc. 5th Symp. Rock Mech.*, Pergamon, Oxford.

GREGORY, A. R. (1963), 'Shear wave velocity measurements of sedimentary rock samples under compression', *Rock Mechanics* (ed. C. Fairhurst), Pergamon, Oxford.

GRIFFITH, A. A. (1924), 'Theory of rupture', *Proc. 1st Int. Cong. App. Mech.*, Delft.

GRIFFITH, D. H. and KING, R. F. (1965), *Applied Geophysics for Engineers and Geologists*, Pergamon, Oxford.

GRIGGS, D. T. (1936), 'Deformation of rocks under high deforming pressure', *J. Geol.*, **44**, 541.

GRIGGS, D. T. (1939), 'Deformation of rocks under high deforming pressure', *J. Geol.*, **47**, 225.

HANDIN, J. and HAGER, R. V. (1958), 'Experimental deformation of sedimentary rocks under confining pressure: tests at high temperature', *Bull. Amer. Assoc. Petr. Geol.*, **42**, 2892.

HANDIN, J. and HAGER, R. V. (1958), 'Experimental deformation of sedimentary rocks under confining pressure: tests at high temperature', *Bull. Amer. Assoc, Petr. Geol.*, **42**, 2892.

HANDIN, J., HAGER, R. V., FEATHER, J. and FRIEDMAN, M. (1963), 'Experimental deformation of sedimentary rocks under confining pressure; pore pressure tests', *Bull. Amer. Assoc. Petr. Geol.*, **47**, 717.

HAST, N. (1958), *Measurement of Rock Pressure in Mines*, Sverige Geol. Unders. Arsbok, 52, Stockholm.

HEARD, H. C. (1963), 'The effect of large changes in strain rate in the experimental deformation of rocks', *J. Geol.*, **71**, 162.

HIRAMATSU, Y. and OKA, Y. (1966), 'Determination of the tensile strength of a rock by compression of an irregular test piece', *Int. J. Rock Mech. Min. Sci.*, **3**, 89.

HOEK, E. (1965a), 'Fracture of anisotropic rock', *Symp. Rock Mechanics & Strata Control in Mines*, S. African Inst. Min. Met., Johannesburg.

HOEK, E. (1965b), 'Design of a centrifuge for the simulation of gravitational force fields in mine models', *Symp. Rock Mech. and Strata Control in Mines*, S. African Inst. Min. Met., Johannesburg.

HOEK, E. (1966), 'Rock mechanics – an introduction for the practical engineer', *Mining Mag.*, **114**, 236.

HOSKING, J. R. (1955), 'A comparison of tensile strength, crushing strength and elastic properties of roadmaking rocks', *Quarry Man. J.*, **39**, 200.

HOWELL, B. F. (1959), *Introduction to Geophysics*, McGraw-Hill, New York.

INGLIS, C. E. (1913), 'Stresses in a plate due to the presence of cracks and sharp corners', *Trans. Inst. Naval Architects*, **55**, 219.

ISAACSON, E. ST Q. (1962), *Rock Pressure in Mines*, Mining Publications, London.

JAEGER, C. (1963), 'Malpasset report', *Water Power*, **15**, 55.

JAEGER, J. C. (1959), 'The frictional properties of joints in rock', *Geophys. pura et appl.*, **43**, 148.

JAEGER, J. C. (1962), *Elasticity, Fracture and Flow*, Methuen, London.

JAEGER, J. C. and COOK, N. G. W. (1963), 'Theory and application of curved jacks for measurement of stresses', *Symp. State of Stress in the Earth's Crust*, Elsevier, New York.

JENKINS, J. D. (1960), 'A laboratory and underground study of the bearing capacity of mine floors', *3rd Int. Conf. on Strata Control, Paris*.

JUDD, W. R. and HUBER, C. (1961), 'Correlation of rock properties by statistical methods', *Int. Symp. on Mining Research* (ed. G. Clarke), Pergamon, Oxford.

KIDYBINSKI, A. (1966), 'Rheological models of Upper Silesian carboniferous rocks', *Int. J. Rock Mech. Min. Sci.*, **3**, 279.

KNOPOFF, L. (1952), 'On Rayleigh wave velocities', *Bull. Seis. Soc. Amer.*, **42**, 307.

KRYNINE, D. P. and JUDD, W. R. (1957), *Engineering Geology and Geotechnics*, McGraw-Hill, New York.

KVAPIL, R. (1963), Contribution to discussion *Symp. State of Stress in the Earth's Crust.* Elsevier, New York.

LANCASTER-JONES, P. F. F. (1966), *Bibliography of Rock Mechanics*, Civil Eng. Res. Assoc., London.

LANE, K. S. and HECK, W. J. (1964), 'Triaxial testing for strength of rock joints', *Proc. 6th Symp. Rock Mech., Univ. Missouri, Rolla.*

LEEMAN, E. R. (1965), 'Measurement of stress in rock', *Symp. Rock Mech. and Strata Control in Mines*, S. African Inst. Min. Met., Johannesburg.

LEET, L. D. (1960), *Vibrations from Blasting Rock*, Harvard Univ. Press, Cambridge, Mass.

LITTLE, A. J., STEWART, J. C. and FOOKES, P. J. (1963), 'Bedrock grouting tests at Mangla Dam', *Symp. Grouts and Drilling Muds in Eng. Pract.*, Butterworths, London.

LOMNITZ, C. (1956), 'Creep measurements in igneous rocks', *J. Geol.*, **64**, 473.

MCCLINTOCK, F. A. and WALSH, J. B. (1962), 'Friction on Griffith cracks in rock under pressure', *Proc. 4th Cong. App. Mech., Berkley*, Amer. Soc. Mech. Engrs, New York.

MENCL, V. (1966), 'Mechanics of landslides with non-circular slip surfaces with special reference to the Vaiont slide', *Géotechnique*, **16**, 329.

MURRELL, S. A. F. and MISRA, A. K. (1962), 'Time dependent strain or creep in rocks and similar materials', *Bull. Inst. Min. Met.*, **71**, 353.

MURRELL, S. A. F. (1963), 'A criterion for brittle fracture of rocks under triaxial stress', *Proc. 5th Symp. Rock Mech.*, Pergamon, Oxford.

NADAI, A. (1950), *Theory of Flow and Fracture of Solids* (Vol. 1), McGraw-Hill, New York.

NADAI, A. (1963), *Theory of Flow and Fracture of Solids* (Vol. 2), McGraw-Hill, New York.

NICHOLLS, H. R. (1961), '*In-situ* determination of the dynamic elastic constants of rock', *Int. Symp. Mining Res.* (ed. G. Clarke), Pergamon, Oxford.

OBERT, L., WINDES, S. L. and DUVALL, W. I. (1946), 'Standardized tests for determining the physical properties of mine rocks', *U.S. Bureau of Mines, Rept Invest.*, 3891.

OBERT, L. and DUVALL, W. I. (1967), *Rock Mechanics and the Design of Structures in Rock*, Wiley, New York.

OROWAN, E. (1951), 'Creep in metallic and non-metallic materials', *Proc. 1st Nat. Cong. App. Mech.*, Amer. Soc. Mech. Engrs., New York.

ORTLEPP, W. D. (1960), 'Approximate determination of shear strength of Witwatersrand quartzite', *J. S. Afr. Inst. Min. Met.*, **61**, 137.

PARSONS, R. C. and HEDLEY, D. G. F. (1966), 'Analysis of the viscous property of rocks for classification', *Int. J. Rock Mech. Min. Sci.*, **3**, 325.

PHILLIPS, D. W. (1948), 'Tectonics of mining', *Colliery Eng.*, **25**, 199.

PHOTODYAKONOV, M. M. (1965), 'Methods of evaluating the cracked state and strength of rocks *in-situ*', *4th Int. Conf. Strata Control and Rock Mech.*, Columbia Univ., New York.

PRANDTL, L. (1924), 'Spannungsverteilung in plastischen Koerpern', *Proc. 1st Int. Cong. App. Mech.*, Delft.

PRICE, N. J. (1960), 'Compressive strength of coal measure rocks', *Colliery Eng.*, **37**, 283.

PRICE, N. J. (1966), *Fault and Joint Development in Brittle and Semi-brittle Rock*, Pergamon, Oxford.

REHBINDER, P. A., SCHREINER, L. A. and ZHIGACH, K. (1948), 'Hardness reducers in drilling', (*Trans.*), *C.S.I.R.*, Melbourne.

REYNOLDS, H. (1961), *Rock Mechanics*, Crosby Lockwood, London.

RICHARDS, C. W. (1961), *Engineering Materials Science*, Chapman & Hall, London.

RINEHART, E. C. (1960), 'Creep of solenhofen limestone under moderate confining pressures', *Mem. Geol. Soc. Amer.*, **79**, 227.

RINEHART, J. S. and PEARSON, J. (1954), *Behaviour of Metals under Impulsive Loads*, Amer. Soc. Metals, Cleveland.

RINEHART, J. S. (1962), 'Effect of transient stress waves in rock', *Int. Symp. Mining Res.* (ed. G. Clarke), Pergamon, Oxford.

ROBERTS, A., HAWKES, I., WILLIAMS, F. T. and DHIR, R. K. (1964), 'A laboratory study of the photo-elastic stressmeter'. *Int. J. Rock Mech. Min. Sci.*, **I**, 441.

ROBERTSON, E. C. (1964), 'Viscoelasticity of rock', *Symp. State of Stress in the Earth's Crust* (ed. W. R. Judd), Elsevier, New York.

RUIZ, M. D. and CAMARGO, F. P. DE (1966), 'Large-scale field test on rock', *Proc. 1st Cong. Int. Soc. Rock Mech.*, Lisbon.

SACK, R. A. (1946), 'Extension of Griffith's theory of rupture to three dimensions', *Proc. Phys. Soc.*, *58*, 729.

SALOMON, M. G. D. (1963), 'Elastic analysis of displacements and stresses induced by the mining of seam or reef deposits', *J. S. Afr. Inst. Min. Met.*, **64**, 128.

SCHON, J. (1966), 'Velocity of longitudinal waves and elastic moduli of dry and saturated sedimentary rocks', *Proc. 1st Cong. Int. Soc. Rock Mech.*, Lisbon, **1**.

SCHWARTZ, A. E. (1964), 'Failure of rock in the triaxial shear test', *Proc. 6th Symp. Rock Mechs.*, *Univ. Missouri, Rolla*.

SELBERG, H. L. (1952), 'Transient compression waves from spherical and cylindrical cavities', *Ark. Phys.*, **5**, 97.

SERDENGECTI, S. and BOOZER, G. D. (1961), 'The effects of strain rate and temperature on the behaviour of rocks subject to triaxial compression', *Penn. State Univ., Min. Inds. Exp. Stn. Bull.*, **76**, 83.

SUTHERLAND, R. B. (1963), 'Some dynamic and static properties of rock', *Proc. 5th Symp. Rock Mech.*, Pergamon, Oxford.

TALWANI, M. and EWING, M. (1960), 'Rapid computation of gravitational attraction of 3-dimensional bodies of arbitrary shape', *Geophysics*, **25**, 181.

TERICHOW, O. and LARSON, W. C. (1967), 'Pendulum sclerometer for surface hardness studies', *U.S. Bureau of Mines, Rept Invest.*, 6952.

TERZAGHI, K. and PECK, R. B. (1948), *Soil mechanics in Engineering Practice*, Wiley, New York.

TIMOSHENKO, S. and GOODIER, J. (1951), *Theory of Elasticity*, McGraw-Hill, New York.

UNITED STATES BUREAU OF RECLAMATION (1953), 'Physical properties of some typical foundation rocks', *Concrete Lab. Rept*, S.P. 39.

WALLIS, R. H., HARLAND, W. B., GEE, D. G. and GAYER, R. A. (1966), *A Scheme of Petrographic Nomenclature for some Metamorphic Rocks in Spitsbergen*, Norsk Polarinst, Arbok.

WEIBULL, W. (1939), 'A statistical theory of the Strength of Materials', *Proc. Roy. Swedish Acad. Eng. Sci.*, **151**.

WINDES, S. (1949), 'Physical properties of mine rock', *U.S. Bureau of Mines, Rept Invest.*, 4459.

WINDES, S. (1950), 'Physical properties of mine rock (2)', *U.S. Bureau of Mines, Rept Invest.*, 4727.

WOODRUFF, S. (1966), *Methods of Working Coal and Metal Mines*, Pergamon, Oxford.

YOUASH, Y. Y. (1966), 'Experimental deformation of layered rock', *Proc. 1st Cong. Int. Soc. Rock Mech. Lisbon*, **1**, 787.

YOUNG, F. M. (1963), 'The secondary breaking effects of high frequency electric energy applied to rock fragments', *Rock Mechanics* (ed. C. Fairhurst), Pergamon, Oxford.

ZIENKIEWICZ, O. C. and STAGG, K. G. (1967), 'Cable method of *in-situ* rock testing', *Int. J. Rock Mech. Min. Sci.*, **4**, 273.

ZIENKIEWICZ, O. C. and CHEUNG, Y. K. (1966), 'Application of the finite element technique to problems of rock mechanics', *Proc. 1st Congr. Int. Soc. Rock Mech., Lisbon*, **1**, 661.

Index

Angle, of failure, 56, 59–68
  of internal friction, 58–65
  of shear plane, 20–8
Anisotropy, 34, 130

Basalt, 13, 14
Bedding planes, 119–20, 158
Bingham model, 42, 44–5
Body wave, 71
Brittle failure, 55–69, 113–14, 168
Brittle material, 30
Buckingham theorum, 164
Bulk modulus, 30, 31
Burger model, 42

Centrifuge, 167–8
Characteristic impedance, 74, 78,
  80–1
Classification of rock,
  design criteria, 155–60
  engineering properties, 155–60
  geological structures, 8–11, 127–
  128
Clay, 2
Cleavage, 120–2
Coefficient, of internal friction, 58–
  65
  of sliding friction, 129
  of viscosity, 42
  mass fracture, 131
Competent rock, 2, 67, 127–8
Compression wave, 71, 74
Compressive strength, 56
  of rocks, 57
  test, 90
  uniaxial, 55–7
Continuity, 33–4
Coulomb–Navier criterion of failure, 58–63
Coulomb theory of failure, 58
Creep, 43–54

constant, 46–53, 156
exponent, 47–53, 156
primary, 45
properties, 46–53
secondary, 45, 117
tertiary, 45, 117
test, 88–9
Criterion of failure, 58–69
  Coulomb–Navier, 58–63
  Griffith, 65–9
  Mohr, 63–5

Deformation, 156–60
  dynamic, 83–5
  effect of water on, 108–9
Deformation structures, 119–32
Density, 15, 16
  effect on rock strength, 16
Design criteria, 155–60
Design in rock, 1, 40, 53–4, 155–68
Design methods, 160–8
  mathematical models, 160–3
  physical models, 163–8
Differential displacement, 77
Dimensional analysis, 163–8
Displacement, 71–2
Ductile behaviour, 113–15
Ductility limit, 114, 134
Dynamic loading, 36, 70–1
Dynamic rock properties, 70–85
  effect of water on, 109–10
  tests, 89–90, 92

Effective stress, 105
Elastic constants, 30–6
  of rocks, 36–9
Elastic limit, 30, 40, 56
Elastic wave motion, 71–80
  velocity of, 74–6
Elasticity,
  dynamic modulus of, 73–4

Elasticity—*contd.*
  effect of pressure on, 112–14
  effect of temperature on, 112–14
  modulus of, 30, 46–53
  of rocks, 33–40
  theory of, 28–31, 40

Failure, 55–69
  Coulomb–Navier criterion, 58–63
  Griffith criterion, 65–9
  Mohr criterion, 63–5
  shear, 56, 58–65
  tensile, 57, 65–9
Failure structures, 119–32
Fatigue, 50, 82
Faults, 124–6
Folds, 120–2
Foliation surfaces, 119–20, 128
  cleavage, 120–2
  schistosity, 120
Fracture interference function, 64–65
Friction, 58
  internal, 58–65
  sliding, 128–9

Gelatine models, 166
Geological classification, 8–11
Geological structures, 119–32
Granite, 13, 14, 159
Gravitational effects – models, 166–8
Griffith criterion of failure, 55–69
Grouting, 138–9

Hardness, 7–8, 83, 92
  scratch, 7
  sclerometer, 8, 83
Heat – effect on rocks, 46, 111–16
Homogeneity, 33–4
Hooke's law, 30
Hookean model, 41
Hugonot equation, 79
Hysteresis, 84–5

Impact toughness, 83, 92
Impedance, 74, 78, 80, 81

Incompetent rock, 127–8
Initial tangent modulus, 36, 156
Internal friction in rocks, 58
  angle of, 58–65
  coefficient of, 58–65
Isotropy, 33–4

Joints, 122–4
  frequency, 123, 158
  spacing, 128, 158
  systems, 122–4, 158

Kelvin–Voight model, 42, 44–6

Lamé constant, 32
Lamination, 119–20
Limestone, 159
Love wave, 75

Mass fracture coefficient, 131
Massive rock features, 119–32
Maxwell model, 42–3
Mechanical properties of rocks, 1
Mineral content of rock, 8–16
  effect on rock properties, 7, 8, 16
Minerals, 4–8
Model, analysis, 163–8
  materials, 165–8
Modulus, bulk, 30, 31
  elastic, 30, 46–53
  of rigidity, 30, 31
Mohr, criterion of failure, 63–5
  envelope, 63–5, 94–5
  strain circle, 24–8
  stress circle, 21–3, 104–5, 128–30
Moisture, 102–9

Newton model, 41
Non-elastic rocks, 34–5, 37, 54, 156

Permanent deformation, 44–5, 116–118
Permeability, 102–4
Photoelasticity, 151, 153, 154
Physical properties of rocks, 4–16
Plane of weakness, 120, 123–6, 128–130, 137
Plane strain, 23–8

Plane stress, 20–2
Plastic flow, 112, 116–18
Poisson's ratio, 31–3, 157
Pore water, 102–9
  content, 106–7
  effects on rock properties, 104–110
  pressure, 104–8
Porosity, 15–16, 102–3
Prager model, 42
Primary creep, 45, 46
Primitive stresses, 111–12, 124
Principal axes, 21, 24
Principal strain, 24
Principal stress, 21

Quartz, 12
  effect on rock strength, 7, 8
Quasi-elastic rocks, 34–5, 37, 40, 54, 156

Rayleigh wave, 75–6
Reinforcement of massive rock, 133–9
  grouting, 138–9
  rock bolting, 135–8
  stress relief, 133–5
Resistivity of rock, 147, 149
Rheological models, 41–5
Rheological rock properties, 41–54
Risk, 1, 35
Rock, 2
  composition, 4–8
  igneous, 8–11
  metamorphic, 10–11
  sedimentary, 9–11
  structure, 11–15
Rockbolts, 97, 135–8
Rock properties
  creep data, 46–9
  density, 15, 16, 38
  dynamic strength, 81–2
  effect of failure structures on, 128–30
  effect of pressure on, 111–18, 147–9
  effect of temperature on, 111–18
  effect of water on, 104–10

  elastic constants, 36–9
  influence of scale on, 130–2
  mineral content, 7, 8, 16
  seismic wave velocities, 74–5
  strength, 7, 8, 16, 30, 38, 39, 57, 62
  tests, 86–99
Rock testing, 86–100
  accuracy, 99–100
  field, 96–9
  laboratory, 86–95
  specimen preparation, 86–7
  triaxial, 92–5
Rock tests, 86–99
  creep, 88–9
  dynamic, 89–90, 92
  field bolt test, 97
  field jack test, 96
  field plate test, 97
  field seismic test, 99
  field shear test, 98–9
  strength, 90–2
  stress/strain characteristics, 86–90
  triaxial, 92–5

St Venant model, 41
Sandstone, 13, 14
Schwedoff model, 42, 45
Secant modulus of elasticity, 35–6
Secondary creep, 45–6, 117
Seismic waves, 71
  absorption constant, 79
  displacement, 76
  frequency, 76
  particle velocity, 76–80
  propagation, 70–81
  propagation constant, 79
  propagation law, 79, 80
  reflection, 80–1
  site factor, 79, 80
  velocity, 72–6, 148
  zone, 71
Semi-elastic rocks, 34–5, 37, 54, 156
Shale, 14, 15, 159
Shear, strain, 23
  strength, 56, 61

Shear—*contd.*
  stress, 20
  wave, 71, 74
Shock wave, 71
Soil, 2
Statistical analysis, 100–1
Stiffness, 30
Strain, 23–9
  at a point, 23–5
  ellipse, 25–8
  finite, 25–8
  in a plane, 23–8
  in wave motion, 78–80
  normal, 23
  quadratic, 27–8
  shear, 23
Strain cell, 146
Strain energy, 124
Strain gauge, 24, 142–4
  rosette, 25, 143–4
Strain measurement, 140–54
  borehole, 144–7
  direct, 142–4
Strain rate, 81–2, 117–18
Stratification, 120
  bedding, 120
  lamellation, 120
  lamination, 120
Strength, 7, 8, 16, 30, 38, 39, 53,
    55–69, 157
  compressive, 56, 57
  effect of failure structures on,
    128–30
  effect of pressure on, 113–15
  effect of strain rate on, 81–2,
    117–18
  effect of temperature on, 113–15
  effect of water on, 104–8
  in confinement, 58–69
  shear, 56, 58–65
  tensile, 57, 65–9
  uniaxial, 55–7
Stress, 17–23, 28–9
  at a point, 17–19

  effective, 105
  in a plane, 20–2
  in wave motion, 78–80
  relief, 133–5
  residual, 124
  triaxial, 22–3
Stress analysis, 17–23
Stress measurement, 140–54
  curved jack, 150
  flat jack, 150–1
  indirect, 149–54
  mechanics of, 141–2
  related to rock properties, 147
  stressmeter, 151, 153, 154
Stress relaxation, 44
Stress relief, 133–5, 150
Stress–strain relationship, 28–33
Surface wave, 71, 75–6

Tangent modulus of elasticity, 36
  initial, 36
Temperature effects in rock, 46
Tensile strength, 56
Tertiary creep, 45, 117
Thermoelastic after-effect, 84
Time-strain effects in rock, 41–54
Triaxial test, 92–5

Visco-elasticity, 41–5
Viscosity, 41–5
  coefficient of, 42

Water in rock, 102–9
Wave equation, 72
Wave motion in rock, 76–8
Wave profile, 75, 76
Wave propagation, 70–81
  law, 79
Wave velocity, 38–9, 72–6
Weibull theory, 132

Yield stress, 42

Zener model, 42, 44–6